THE
BODY
MINDSET

Using the Power
of Your Mind to
Change Your Body

Tina R. Allen

Shaelee K. Phillips

ACKNOWLEDGMENTS

I would like to acknowledge the people who assisted me in making this book a reality, especially my daughter, Shaelee Allen, who co- authored parts of it and is the model for the cover. She is one of the most genuine, positive, and healthy people I know. Special thanks also go to my brother, Steven Austin and good friend, Jeff Stagg who helped to mentor me and guide me through the publishing process, and to Rob Wingfield who designed the website and support material for this program. Thanks also goes to my five other children who inspire me on our joint journey to mental and physical health and were so supportive of me during my transformation, and to my partner and friend, Gary Garcia, who is by my side in this and all my other adventures.

DEDICATION

I dedicate this book to my six kids who are wise beyond their years and are both my support and the source of my inspiration.

Table of Contents

PART ONE – BODY MINDSET

MINDSET SKILLS

PART TWO -MINDSET RETREAT

PERSONAL CARE

CREATE A PLAN

MEET THE AUTHORS

Shaelee K Phillips

I remember the moment I realized the power my thoughts had on my fitness. I was running on the treadmill (aka the dreadmill), and I hated every minute of it.

I kept thinking about how stupid this was and how out of shape and fat I had become. I had just had my second daughter, Hayzlee in April, and I had boycotted working out during my entire pregnancy. I was not happy with my new mom-body and only had a month or so to get in shape for the summer. To me at that time, working out was a way to make my body look better and nothing more. My feet felt heavy, and with every step, I was certain I was going to die. After what felt like forever, I checked my distance and I'd barely hit the one-mile mark. I figured it was good enough and I called it quits.

The next time I was on the treadmill, I brought my music. The songs that came up on my iPod were random, each one having a different effect on my running performance. Some songs made me feel sad and weak, some made me feel alive and strong, while other songs just straight pissed me off. The vibes were all over the place and so were my thoughts. Soon, I was so frustrated and exhausted that I started skipping through the songs rapidly hoping to find one that could save me. After nearly falling off the treadmill, I hit the stop button and checked the distance, barely 2 miles.

From this I learned a few things that made fitness work better for me:

1.   Music has a powerful influence on your feelings and moods.

2.   Using music you love during fitness can elevate your thoughts and improve your physical performance.

3.   Your thoughts define your performance.

AND

4.   I was going to need a better playlist...

Find a Way to Hold Yourself Accountable

After creating a better playlist and becoming a little more aware of my thoughts, I was able to hit a new personal record on the treadmill: 4 miles straight and I was feeling good.

Then, my mom called and told me she signed my husband and I up for a half marathon and I literally laughed out loud.

I thought back to the days when I was a cheerleader in high school. I was in the best shape of my life. I was working out every morning and 5 times a week after school, and I still couldn't run more than 3 miles at a time. How was I going to run 13 miles straight?

But, if my mom was committed to do it, so was I.

@ShaeKaeFitness

MY OWN TRANSFORMATION

Just a year earlier, my mom, who had been going through her own transformation, had run her first half marathon. She eventually convinced me to join her by saying "If I can do it, so can you."

At that point I was committed and not about to waste her money and let her down. That was just the accountability I needed to help me get serious.

A Change of Mindset

When I started, I hated working out. I only saw it as something I needed to do to get back in shape after the babies. Now, fitness is my therapy, love, energy, and joy. Working out makes me happier. Fitness takes away my blues and relieves my stress. For me, working out is a way of training my mind and body to be stronger. It is a mind game I play with myself.

During my second half marathon, my phone quit working and I didn't have my perfect playlist to help me. It was then that I tapped into my thoughts to keep me going and realized that was all I really needed. My music helped me get there, but those vibes were inside me. They were part of me, and I could feel them whenever I wanted to.

I love fitness because it makes me stronger mentally and physically. I have made it my goal to share that love with others. Once you break through those glass ceilings, as my mom calls it, you feel brave and strong, and you know you can break through everything else in life.

For me, fitness is a path to total self-improvement at every level.

With husband Bray, about six months
into my third pregnancy

My Advice to You

If I could share some advice that
helped me along the way,
it would be:

Track Your Progress

Hold Yourself Accountable

Find a workout you love doing.

Don't be so serious, have fun!

Keep your head in the right place

And quit giving up

Learn to love and appreciate e your body through every stage of life, whether it's having children, breastfeeding, getting in shape, or getting older. Just love yourself and be the best you can be.

My latest loves are pole fitness, hiking, running, coaching, and facilitating Body Mindset courses with my mom, but my focus, of course will always be my husband and three beautiful children.

Besides being into fitness, mindset, and positive vibes, I teach second grade, run a preschool in the summer, and stay connected with my family and siblings.

Thanks for joining us on this wonderful adventure, and I hope to connect with you again in more of our projects.

Shaelee Kae Phillips

MEET THE AUTHORS

Tina R. Allen

I'm excited to be writing this book with my daughter, Shaelee, not only because she is so amazing and inspirational, but she is also one of my favorite people to be around. I think our different physical experiences will help us be able to meet more people where they are.

As a child, I never felt comfortable in my own skin or physical ability. In fact, I avoided it whenever I could. I had to change many of the views I had of me and what I could do before I could stay on course and stick with my body goals. When I did, I lost nearly a hundred pounds.

I finally did it and with the right mindset so can you!

PREFACE – YOUR BODY MATTERS

I've been overweight, or thought I was, for most of my adolescent and adult and life. Regardless of what the scale said, when I looked in that mirror, a fat person who hatted fitness and didn't have willpower looked back. I was in the mindset to be heavy and out of shape even when I starved myself to the place that the scale said I was not.

Most of my life, no matter what I tried, I was less that successful with my attempts to change the direction I was going with myself physically. It's not like I didn't try. I probably tried every diet out there. I would set my goals, make a plan, buy a book, get a gym pass, or whatever I thought it took, but for whatever reason, I would leave that track and sabotage that goal, without even being aware that I did.

If I ate something I shouldn't, or got into an emotional place that I shouldn't be in, it spiraled me out of control physically as the waves of, "I've messed this up again", "But, "I'm off track anyway" and "I need this to help me feel better" and washed over me.

For decades, I had a personal battle with my weight. And I could seem to break out of that or make some headway. For years of that, I even threw in the towel and gave trying. I wasn't until I got my head in the right place that I was able to pull out of that and find a way to get it done.

If you too have been in something that feels like a losing battle with your body, or you've reached the place where you are about to give, I know how much that hurts. We are never in a darker place than when we don't feel like we are enough In some area of our lives.

We feel extensive personal pain anytime we don't feel like we have control over ourselves and our destiny in ANY area of our life. One of the most basic needs is to know that we have control and we can make decisions that will lead to our own destiny. The power of choosing my own mindset gave me back the control I needed over my life and my body.

I had to get back in my own place of power to take control of that. When I did I lost almost a hundred pounds that had been weighting me down.

I feel lucky to have run into the right combination of people, education, and thoughts that got me there, and I hope that by sharing that mental place that made me effective, I can help you get there too.

BEFORE WE CAN BE EFFECTIVE WITH ANYTHING, WE MUST GET INTO AN EFFECTIVE PLACE IN OUR MIND SO WE CAN.

Mindset is the lens we look through when we see ourselves and the world. Our ability to look at things from different perspectives gives us control over who we are, what we do and how we feel.

Life deals us the hands that it does. Much of life is random and unfiltered. It is our choice of the glasses we choose to see things through that gives us power over how we feel, who we are and where we want to go in all that. The winds of life are not always our choice, but by adjusting our sails of mindset and direction, we get control over our own direction and where we go in all that.

It took me years (probably decades) to discover that the reason I continued to be heavy even though I was trying, is that I never completely got in the mindset it takes to do it effectively. I never got effective with weight loss or body change in my mind.

When I finally got serious and let myself get competent to do this in my mind, it made a RADICAL DIFFERENCE in the direction I was going with my body.

All those 'reasons' I thought I had, were still in my life, but mentally, I wouldn't let them be seen as roadblocks. Sure, the challenges were still there. All the things that made it hard in my life were still there, but instead of letting myself see them roadblocks, I made myself look past them and keep my eyes on that success. Instead of roadblocks, I saw my stress, lack of time and personal challenges as an obstacle course that I would figure out how to get through.

I looked those challenges square in the face and said, "Oh yeah, if you think this is going to stop me, then you don't know me!"

When we get our heads into a competent and determined place with something, it radically changes our ability to do it successfully. Being in the right mental place changed what I mentally did that made me powerless and ineffective, including what I did to myself when I failed.

Gone were the mental justifications for eating wrong and not working out. Gone was spiraling down into that ineffective rabbit hole of pity and self-loathing that fueled a binge when I failed. Once I committed to stay in a healthy and powerful place in my mind, I began to see all the knowledge and data that was in the slips that I made. Without all that dangerous loathing and self judgement, I found that each slip that I made gave me another piece of knowledge about what doesn't work for me. By getting out of that emotionally self-destruct place that fuels our failure and getting into a place of body competence I didn't know I had, I was able to RADICALLY change both my body and the way I was physically going in my life.

It was then that I was on to something very powerful. If I, someone who had felt physically incompetent much of my life, could get into a different mental place where I was, and by doing so lose nearly a hundred pound and change how I felt both inside and out, just by changing my mindset, then so could others.

If I could help other find body success and feel the way that felt, then it was critical that I write down and pass on mindsets and ways of thinking that helped me do it. It was by getting into a mental place that I didn't even know I could be in, one of body competence, that I was dramatically able to change my body and the way I lived my physical life. It was then that I coined the term, Body Mindset in my own head. To get competent with my own body, I just had to find 'The Body Mindset' that would make me able to do it.

Competence at something doesn't happen until you enter the place where you are mentally competent with that in your mind.

Physical competence, like all other competence, comes from getting into the mental place that makes you competent in your minds. With our bodies, just like anything else, we MUST get into a place that will make us effective and competence in our minds so we can!

In the wrong mental place, you will spin your wheels in frustration with what seems like a lack of ability or willpower to change your body. When you get in the place that makes you successful in your mind, you will physically and resiliently get on the track it takes to do it. Yes, you can! It is the place you are at in your mind that matters.

WE MUST CHANGE THE PRIORITY OF MINDSET AND HEALTH

As Shaelee and I got ready to publish this book, our world experienced the Corona Virus shut down. Initially, we saw this shutdown as a roadblock in the way of our goals and our life and we felt frustrated, as most of us did when this pandemic interrupted our lives.

Initially, we thought, "Society won't shut down, wear masks, or change their lives to that extent because we are all too busy to do it!" Then, a global pandemic came along and showed us that we better quit putting other things in front of our health. We better change the priority and move things in our lives out of way of our health.

As writers, Shaelee and I initially decided to put this book we were writing on hold because, with a worldwide threat to our global health on our minds, the contents of our book didn't seem all that important. We couldn't have been more wrong. Our world was in the middle of what would be the biggest shift in the way we saw and moved things out of the way for health in our lifetime.

> *Most of the problems we have with our weight or our body goals comes from priority. We can't do it because it hasn't yet become essential to us that we do.*

We can't do it because we put our bodies and our own self-care in last place in our lives and our minds.

We often can't accomplish our body goals until we change the priority we put on doing them in our minds

---

Priority is a huge problem when it comes to our body goal, because until it becomes a true personal priority to us that we do, we won't find a way to make it fit in our already busy lives.

Before our body goals will fit, it must become a priority to us that we accomplish these things. We must also get into the mental place where IT MATTERS and it becomes a real personal priority to us to accomplish this thing before we will be able to make it fit in our lives.

No matter who you are, you have what it takes to lose, even tremendous amounts of weight. You have what it takes to get in a tremendously different place with your body. It just has to becomes a truly personal priority to you that you do.

WE JUST CHANGED THE PRIORITY OF OUR HEALTH WITH COVID

When something become a priority, we find a way to do it. This pandemic just gave us a mental makeover when it comes to the priority we put on health in our lives.

We just proved to ourselves that we will move heaven and earth to take care of our health when we believe we are in danger of losing it. We all did things that we thought were impossible before Covid in the name of our health. Whether it was wearing a mask, changing the way we work, travel or hangout with family and friends, we all sacrificed and made changes in our lives in the name of our health. We just proved that when health matters, we can, and we will!

We don't really need more time, or money or more energy or fewer problems the way we think we do. We just need more priority, because when something matter to us enough, we will find a way to remove all the other obstacles and get it done. If there is one thing we learn from Covid-19, it is that we can find time for our health when our priority is right. Take away the option to fail, and we will find a way to take care of our health the way that we should. Surprisingly, we can learn about how to make time for our self-care from a global pandemic.

WE MUST PRIORITIZE OUR MENTAL CARE AS WELL

And it is not just our physical health that is at risk when we fail to take care of ourselves. It is mental and emotional health as well.

One reason we must take care of our bodies, is that doing so is so intertwined with the way we feel emotionally. Most of us DO NOT mentally feel the way we should until we get on the track, we should be on physically. Until we feed and care for our bodies the way that we should, we don't feel the way we should in our lives.

Our minds and bodies are connected to the point, that it is not just physical things we fix when we do better with our body goals.

So much of the depression, self-loathing, and feelings of powerlessness that take away the quality of our lives, comes from not physically taking care of ourselves the way that we should. Until we eat and get physically active the way that we should, we will continue to feel weak, depressed and stuck the way that we do.

One reason to change the priority of your body goals is that it will mentally and emotionally change the way you feel when you do.

CHANGE THE PRIORITY OF YOUR GOAL

Before we can ever get effective with our bodies, we have to mentally make it matter. Until it becomes a true personal priority, we won't get effective at doing it.

Really, there is nothing more important than your personal self-care and you MUST take care of yourself and your body the way you should because ALL your other priorities depend on you!

YOU TO BE THERE for everything else that matter to you. You are the central component of all of your goals. You must have the health, energy, focus, and self-esteem that takes to do well with your other priorities and to get that, you MUST take care of your nutrition and your health. Your health matters and you must put that first in your life because all of your priorities depend on you!

Like putting your own oxygen mask on first, you MUST prioritize taking care of yourself and your own body first in your life.

If there is thing we take away from this pandemic, it must be that we must change the value we place on our own health in our lives. It has to matter to us enough that we put it in first.

Steven Covey, one of the most influential writers and speakers of our time put it this way, the big rocks (or things that matter) in our lives won't fit in them until we mentally and physically put them in first.

We took care of ourselves during Covid-19 when it wasn't easy because for a time, we made our health one of our top personal priorities. We can do that with the parts of staying healthy, like eating right and working out as well, if we get our heads in the place to insist that we do.

> ## *We make something become possible when we decide that it matters enough that it is!*

Shaelee and I were writing this book when Covid-19 first shut us down. At first Covid-19 this also shut us down as writers, because with a global pandemic on our minds, this book seemed to pale in significance. However, when we changed the way we saw it, we decided that the mindset of health and the information in this book is too valuable to put it back on the shelf during Covid-19 and we doubled down our effort to get it done.

Like Covid-19, the only way we will make our body goals fit is when we make them a priority and decide that it matters to us that they do.

HOW EFFECTIVE IS YOUR MINDSET?

One of the most important skills we will even learn in life is metacognition. Ask yourself if the way you are seeing yourself or something else is making you the way you want to be and getting you where you want to go.

> *Ask yourself if the place you are at in your head will get you where you want to go. If not, change it.*

Being able to look at the effectiveness of your own mindset is a life changing skill. Ask yourself, "Is this way of seeing things giving me the power to get where I want to be?" If you're the state of your mind and the contents of your thoughts and beliefs are not making you effective or happy then maybe, it is time to change them.

Getting your body in a better place. Like everything else, is a product of your thoughts, perception, and belief. Learn to get yourself back in the place of power and ability you need to in to accomplish the goals you set for yourself and your body and you will.

A NO EXCUSES POLICY

One of the most powerful changes you can make in your life is to make a goal, set a path, and create a NO EXCUSE POLICY for yourself to follow it.

We MUST quit getting derailed by our own excuses. We must quit justifying and talking ourselves out of eating right and working out in our own minds. We must take power away from our own excuses, turn them off, quit listening to all the mental persuasion not to, and JUST SAY NO to that chubby little devil on our shoulder and all those mental justifications we allow in our head that let us out of it.

Our own excuses wreak havoc on our results,

Our excuses take us down, but only to the extent

that we are willing to listen to and entertain them

in our minds.

By just saying "No" and refusing to listen to and entertain our own excuses, we gain power over the directions and results we have in our lives.

We must make a NO EXCUSE POLICY, for ourselves and quit giving power to all the excuses we give power to get us out of it in our heads.

There is a place in your head where your problems are too big, your abilities and determination are too small and life throws things at you that make it impossible for you to do. Excuses make us blame everything but ourselves. They sound good, but with the blame, they take something we need to never let go of, our power.

In short, commit to quit listening to the voices inside your head that try to talk you out of.

Tell your resistant self and body,

THE CHOICE HAS BEEN MADE

YOU WANT TO EAT, EAT THIS

AND YOU'RE GOING TO WORKOUT

SO QUIT TALKING ABOUT IT.

You must quit listening to that part of yourself that wants to sabotage you into going in the wrong direction.

One of the most powerful things I did for my own body goal was to make a NO EXCUSE POLICY for myself in my head. Before that, I would wake up and start asking myself how I felt. I would scan my mood and energy and what was going on in my life to see if I could handle my workout or eating plan today. Not surprisingly, more times that not, I talked myself out of it.

As soon as you allow weakness or you start that battle with that persuasive little fat guy who wants pizza on your shoulder, you are going to lose. Once you start even considering the 'reasons' better called excuses in your head, you've already lost because there will always be a reason you can use to justify your way out of it.

> Don't spend any more mental time or energy on the mental battle of it. Don't allow the option for failure by spending mental energy on whether you should or you feel like doing it today.

Real happiness and success comes.
from mastering your own excuses.

Don't allow any more of that 'poor me, I'm so tired, sad, it's so hard and I can't do thought in your head.

Don't allow yourself to use your life or the bad day you just had to justify yourself into skipping that workout or eating some sugar. Those excuses be tempting, but their enticement is a trap, because the moment you give into that thing you think will make you feel better, you almost instantly feel worse.

> Make a one-time decision that you are going to do this.
> Make a NO EXCUSE POLICY in your own head
> and don't indulge in reasons why you can't!

Set your mental rules and no matter what, stick with them. In fact, quit looking at or considering the alternative all together. For example, if you have decided to eat low carb, then only allow yourself to consider or think about the low carb options you have. Quit considering the things outside your solution and you'll quit that battle you have with eating them.

If you have decided to eat vegan, then look only at all the beautiful, wonderful, plant-based options we have in our world. Don't consider anything else. If you are not eating sugar, quit telling yourself you deserve it because you had a bad day. Get out of that pity party in your head about your breakup or the way your boss talked to you today at work. Quit mentally justifying and considering the options for doing something else in your head and you'll stop the battle you have with your body goals.

Failure always happens first in our heads. It happens because we mentally justify why we can't, and we persuade ourselves not to and excuse ourselves from the blame. We are essentially a double agent, with a very persuasive part of ourselves at wants to fail, while another wants to succeed. That sets us up to have a major civil war over every part of it in our minds.

If your choice for the path to body success is intermittent eating, then mentally shut off the options to eat at other times. Get out of the room. Get busy. Get away from temptation and quit considering whether or not you can do this.

Take away the option
to fail and you quit failing.

When you quit looking at and considering the things you shouldn't eat or you quit considering talking yourself out of working out or doing what you should, those things get easier to do. When you focus on the beauty in the things you have chosen to do, you quit suffering and start to get happy in the path that you chose.

I have a quote in my bedroom that says, "The secret to having it all is to realize you already do." That is just as just as try of being happy in a healthy life as it is to being happy in life in general. Let your happiness be here, in the path and the foods that you chose and quit looking at considering the rest.

You can be happy in a healthy life. You just have to get
into the mindset that will make you happy in that life.
That is just as true of the way you eat and workout as it is with any other part of your life. Quit looking over the neighbor's fence and considering the are outside your yard and you will learn to get happy and successful on the path you chose.

Most of the battle we have with losing weight, the struggle we have with fitness and the failure we have at body goals exists because of what we are doing with these things mentally in our heads.

Take away the option to fail and you quit failing. Take away the option to suffer over it and you quit suffering over it. Close the door on junk food and open the door on all the beautiful and healthy options you get. If you are hungry enough that you should be eating at all, the things you should have will begin to taste good when you eat them.

Equally, much of the battle we have with fitness is the mental battle of it as well. Most of the battle of fitness doesn't happen on the court or in the gym. It happens before you put on your shoes or push play on that workout video. Most of the battle of fitness happens in your own head BEFORE you do it.

Make a NO EXCUSES POLICY for yourself in your mind. Refuse to suffer or mentally battle with it in your mind. Let all the challenge of fitness and eating right be spent on getting through it physical and refuse to allow any of that challenge or suffering you do with it in your head.

Take away the option to fail, and quit flirting with whether or not you will, and you will find that you have what it takes to get through today. Get through today, and tomorrow will get easier to do. By getting and staying in the right mental place, you will find that losing weight and getting fit will be something that you will be able to do.

Take away the option to fail,
and you quit failing.
Take away the option to suffer about
eating right and working
out and being healthy
is easier than you think!

START WHERE YOU ARE

If like me you gained weight or lost ground during Covid-19, don't beat yourself up over it. The day you are reading this book is a brand-new day. Today is the option for a fresh new physical start.

If you gained weight, or are not where you want to be physically, don't sweat it. You're in good company. For many of us, Covid-19 was the number of pounds we saw the scale go in the wrong direction.

It doesn't matter where you are on the very wide spectrum of body shape or ability. Start where you are and get in the mental place it takes to decide where you are going to go from here.

Once you are in the mindset it takes to do it, it doesn't matter where that starting place was or how far you need to go. Once you are committed to go in the right direction, and you get on track and in a good daily routine that will get you there, all you have to do is follow the plan and stay the course, AND YOU WILL.

AVOID THE DEMONS OF DISCOURAGEMENT

Perhaps our biggest enemies to life or our body goal are the demons of negativity and discouragement that make us think we are not enough or we don't have what it take to do it.

There is always negativity, pain and the demons of discouragement behind all of those spirals of emotion and behavior that cause us to spin out of control in the wrong direction with our lives and body in the first place. Negativity and THE WRONG MENTAL PLACE, fuels all of the really bad behavior we do with our bodies. In achieving our body goal, it is essential that we keep our head on that place of power and determination that gives is the ability to do it.

One thing to avoid is expecting to lose those 30lbs in 20 days that we see advertised. Weight loss is far more individual and less linear than we thought. We might need to eat fewer calories, wait longer or workout more than someone else, and we need to mental stamina and resilience that will make us abo to stay the course.

> It is nearly always negative emotion
>
> that fuels the fire and spirals us out
>
> of control in the wrong direction.

Refuse to allow the Demon of Discouragement to take you to places you have no good reason to go. One thing you can count on as you lose weight or get in shape, is that things will not go as planned. It may take longer than you think. You may need fewer calories than you think. The pounds won't drop off as consistently as you planned, or they will and then you will reach a plateau where things won't move at all no matter what you try. You will reach a point where you have two choices, get discouraged or change what you do until you get effective.

Mentally get in this for the long haul. Don't expect 30lbs in 20 days. Don't expect it to be easy. Get resilient by expecting to do whatever it takes to get that weight to budge so you can get where you want to be.

In addition, mentally prepare for what you will do when you make a mistake or mentally slip at what you had planned to do.

Not only will biological changes in your body not go the way you expect them to, your own behavior will slip at some point in the process as well. Be mentally prepared to not be on a slippery mental slope when it does.

Be ready for things to not to work out the way you think they will. Be ready to learn from and not slip emotionally when you fall. Get mentally ready for it to be hard and it won't break you when it is.

NOTE: PREPARING FOR IT TO BE HARD is the opposite of what most programs that are selling you. They like to promise that you won't ever be hungry or need to give up anything that you want. Most programs set quick and easy results because that is what people want to buy. They mentally make you breakable in your body goal because they set you up to expect it to be fast and easy. Selling you easy, may be what you want to hear, but it rarely gives you the mental or physical stamina and determination to stick with your goals and get where they want to go.

We can't control how long it will take us to lose the weight or get where we want to go. We can't control our metabolism (excepts with exercise.) We can't control the basic number of calories we need to reach a negative calorie balance in our lives (except with exercise.) Get your head in the place to handle that struggle and it won't *stop you from getting where you want to be!*

Life will through you curve balls. There will always be things outside our circle of control (Like this pandemic.) You will find foods and situations that trigger your bad behavior. What you mentally do with the hard stuff is just as important as the powerful, positive, motivated place you need to get in when you start.

Part of mindset is preparing to sustain your effort for the long haul. As you get into the mindset you need to be successful with your body in this book, remember to reframe the struggle, refuse to suffer, and get into a place that makes you competent to do it as you go.

It always amazes me at the difference changing the place you are at in your head with something changes the way you feel and the perform in the things that you do. Get your head in the right place, and you can be successful and possibly even learn to love the challenge of getting in shape and getting your body where you want it to be.

Get your head in the place that will give you the power and determination you need to go in the right direction with your body and successfully, and you will.

In any situation you can't control,

there is ALWAYS something you can.

MINDSET CHANGES EVERYTHING

Mindset is the universal game changer of our lives. It is also the game changer we need for our body goals. The way you choose to see thing dramatically changes who you are and the power you are with the things you face and do.

Mindset dramatically changes the game for many things in our lives. Mindset dramatically changes our effectiveness with our body goals. In fact, it dramatically changes your effectiveness of everything that you do. In the right mindset you will be able to get your body to a dramatically different place. There is a mindset that will help you get your body where you want it to be. Shaelee and I strongly believe:

There is nothing in the world

That a change of mindset can't improve.

Change your mindset and you will find the power

It takes to choose the body you live your life in!

Tina R Allen,

Shaelee K. Phillips,

The Body Mindset

Connect with us at thebodymindsetbook.com, and coachifyme.com. and with Shaelee @shaekaefitness or on Facebook. We hope to see you there.

MEET ME

Here I am. If you knew me, you would know I am the last girl you would ever expect to write a book about Body or Fitness. I have never been the poster child for body, but I have always been a believer in mindset. I struggled with weight and inactivity my whole teenage and adult life. I thought there must be something wrong with me because no matter how hard I tried, I couldn't get my eating, weight, or body under control.

Finally, after hundreds of diets a lifetime of frustration, I got lucky enough to find the solution that worked for me. I found the power of mindset. It was never me or my body that caused me to struggle with my body goals. It was my mind. Luckily, I learned the trick. The only real way to change your body is to get into the mental place it takes to make it happen.

I didn't need another diet I wouldn't follow anyway. I needed to get mentally and physically in control of me. I needed to change my mindset and make a new kind of commitment to my own health and wellness on the inside. I needed to make a set of mental and physical rules I could commit to follow for a lifetime. I needed a new way to look at myself and a new way to look at food and fitness. I spent a decade of my life being obese when all I needed was a new Body Mindset.

When I finally got into that mindset, I quit fighting myself and the process. I got active. I changed my eating. I lost nearly a hundred pounds and kept that off for nearly ten years. Out of self-disclosure, when I quit going to the gym, I gained the Covid-19 like many of the rest of us. Now, I too am wrapping my head around that again and getting back on track. The difference is this time I know I can!

MEET SHAELEE

More about me later. For now, let me introduce you to Shaelee, my daughter and the cover model and co-author of this book. Shaelee is, in my mind, one of the best Body Mindset Coaches on the planet, and as her mother, I got to watch her own Body Mindset progress and develop.

In the lineup of siblings, Shaelee was third. Just 16 months ahead of her uber-athletic sister Brianna, and right between two naturally twiggy sisters, Shaelee often grew up feeling bigger and less talented than she was. While her sister Bri ran track, played soccer, and excelled in gymnastics. Shaelee said, "I'm tired on Mondays." In our family, the role of athletic sister was taken, and Shaelee's body image often suffered in comparison.

Instead, Shaelee became the academic one. By 6th grade, her talents in math were recognized and she was placed in an advanced math group. She excelled in school until junior high where she tried on the role of ditsy blond that she thought was expected of her as a cheerleader. Luckily, by high school Shaelee found a better balance between social life and education. One day in college, Shaelee called me, frustrated with herself for getting an A- in Calculus. I had to remind her that she was also eight months pregnant and taking 18 credit hours that semester, and she need to give herself a break. After college, Shaelee became a teacher and a math specialist, and after the birth of her second child, she began the mental and physical transformation that got her where she is now.

In her ever-bubbly, upbeat way, Shaelee discovered dance, pole fitness, dance, running, healthy eating, and coaching and she began to motivate and encourage everyone else around her physically as well. Now, she is an incredibly fit and motivating Body Mindset and Fitness coach, a teacher, and a mother of three. Now, in addition to co-author of this book, Shae is a force for positivity, healthy eating, mindset, and fitness on social media as well.

You can join her on Instagram @Shaekaefitness and find both of us online at coachifyme.com and thebodymindsetbook.com.

MEET MY MOM

LET ME INTRODUCE YOU to another very important person in my life.

 This is my Mom. Sadly, her story plays an important part in my own body mindset transformation because her health problems were the inspiration for it. At age 57, my beautiful, selfless mom who had spent a lifetime loving and caring for us while putting herself last had a life-changing stroke that took away her ability to take care of herself or her body. My Mom was a beautiful ray of sunshine. She connected deeply even with strangers. She saw beauty and light in everyone.

She laughed, played joked, cried. Mostly, she loved connected with people more deeply than anyone I know. Sadly, that stroke, took 20 years of quality and ability away from her life, and she was never the same aft she had it.

Mom planned on losing weight and taking better care of herself as soon as her kids were grown. Sadly, she lost the ability to do that just as she reached the age where she had the kind of freedom she had waited for. I felt pain and helplessness after my mom's stroke, but in addition I was scared, because as a single overweight mother myself, I knew I was physically following in my mother's footsteps. If I did not figure how to do it amid the challenge of my life, mom's story would likely be my own.

Mom didn't get to be there for her kids and grandkids the way she dreamed of. Of course, they loved her, but my kids didn't get to know or communicate with her the way I did. Mom helped me realize that taking care of my body is not an option. It is a right, a responsibility, and a privilege. That knowledge came a huge personal cost to my mom, and I was determined not to let that knowledge be lost. My Mom's story helped me realize that I needed to change the priority of my physical-care and quit excusing myself from it. For this, and so many other things, I will always be eternally grateful to my Mom.

COME SEE US IN UTAH

To help you be successful and get the help you need, Shaelee and I offer two other services that will dramatically help you get into the mental place it takes to do it.

First, we offer online coaching and accountability with us or someone else who can help you online. If you need someone to help, you get in the right mental place and help you through the process of accomplishing your body goal, visit our coaching website: www.coachifyme.com

We also would love to invite you to join us at a Mindset Retreat in person with us here in Utah. This retreat is generally on a weekend, or longer if you choose It is help at a resort in Utah, where we will focus on eating right, mentally connecting, and getting back on track with our minds and our bodies.

Sometimes you just need to get away from it all to get going on a new track mentally and physically in your life.

A retreat is a fun and relaxing getaway that includes guided mental and physical tours that will help you get back on track with your mind and body. Come get away, eat delicious food, see the scenery, connect with us and others, and mentally and physically come out in a better place where you can.

Sometimes we need to get away to get our heads in a completely different place. A Body Mindset Retreat will let you get away from everything at home so you can focus and get the guidance and support you need to get going on a new physical path or take it to a new level.

Join us at a 3- and 5-day Mindset Retreats you will spend at a resort with us here in Utah. Come spend time with us, and small group of others at your level. Here we will spend a week or a few days getting back on track with eating good, nutritious food, and getting your head and body going in the right direction.

DIGITAL COACHING

Another service we offer is digital coaching from wherever you are. Physical distance no longer separates us like it once did and we can coach you ourselves or One of us or our staff can coach you and offer you the accountability and support you need to lose the weight you want and get on a healthier and better track.

We can connect and support you in your journey in a variety of ways. We can connect through zoom, hangouts, text or by phone. If it is not practical for you to join us person, but you really feel like you need some help and support to make this work for you, consider signing up for online coaching. You pick the method and schedule of connection that works best for you and you will get the mental and physical support you need to make you successful at your physical goal.

Shaelee and I know that many of us need someone to help support us through the process. We nearly always do better with our body goals when we have support, connection, coaching and accountability.

To help people have the level of support they need, Shaelee and I offer coaching at a distance to give you an option to get the help you need to get on track toward your body goals. Join us in the programs we provide to help you get where you want to be. We would love to see you there.

Until I got my mind in a different place, I couldn't lose the weight or get effective with my body goals. Getting myself in a different place mentally was what it took for me to get effective with my body goals physically.

CHAPTER

ONE

MINDSET

MATTERS

Our minds and bodies are tied together in ways we don't yet fully understand. What we do know is that the way we think and see things dramatically affects many things about our lives and bodies.

The way we see things changes everything

about our power and emotion. Choose to see

yourself and other things in ways that makes you

feel the way you need to feel, do what you need

to do and get where you want to go.

~ Tina Allen

Only when our heads are in our place of power and competence our we able to be our best and do things to the full extent of our ability. Mindset dramatically affects nearly everything about our lives. Of course, it also dramatically affects the way we live our lives physically, and the success we have with our body goals.

To get successful with our body goals, we must get our head in the place it takes to get there. Far too many of us are less than successful with our bodies because we are in less than successful places in our heads when it comes to all things physical in our lives. We are not competent physically, because we don't see ourselves that way and we are not successful with our body goals because we don't see ourselves being successful with them.

When we feel incompetent physically, we don't perform competently. To get our bodies to the places we want them to be, must get our heads in the place it takes to get there. All of us, from world class athletes to those who are out of shape and unhappy with the way we look, must get into a mindset of power, competence and belief to get to the place where we can improve or perform at our best.

Mindset is the prerequisite for success in every area of our lives. Of course, we must also get into the place it takes to get our bodies to a better place as well.

ATHLETES HAVE MINDSET

Professional and world-class athletes and their coaches and trainers know how dramatically mindset affects our physical goals. Athletes and coaches know that the mindset of those athletes dramatically affects the way they perform and the things they physically achieve.

Of course, an athlete must have talent and practice, but top athletes and coaches know that it is their mindset that give athletes that edge. It is the place their minds are in that determines if they perform at the top of their game or if they don't.

Mindset affects our physical performance. There is no one in the athletic field that questions that. We know that the place an athletes mind is in has a dramatic impact on his or her performance. Athletes and their trainers are convinced of the power mindset has on the effectiveness of their physical performance. Those of us who want to lose weight or get in better shape often don't know how greatly the place we are at in heads affect our success with our goals as well.

Even though those of us who want to lose weight or get fit have different goals than those athletes, the mindset it takes to be on top of our game physically is the same for all of us.

Mindset gives us that edge of success. It has a tremendous effect on our ability to accomplish our physical goals as well. No matter where we are on that very wide spectrum of physical shape and performance, we all need the mindset and to get into the mental place in our heads that will make us effective at getting where they physically want to go.

No matter where you are with your body, there is a mindset associated with it. In one mental place, you will eat and perform like this. In another one, you will eat, perform and look and become like that. There is a mindset associated with where you are right now with your body, and another one associated with where you would really like to be.

The problem is most of us don't know that. Most of us who struggle with our bodies or sticking with our body goals have no idea that the problem is just a mindset. Athletes get help with mindset. They have coaches and teams and sports psychologists to help them get into the place they mentally need to be and to point it out to them and help them when they're not.

Those of us who are not athletes seldom get help with the mindset it takes to achieve our physical goals. We may get help with the diet, or the workout or get told what we need to do for the physical part of getting where we want to go, but no one helps us getting into the mental place it takes to get there.

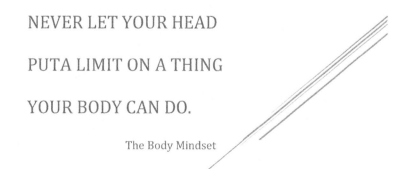

NEVER LET YOUR HEAD

PUT A LIMIT ON A THING

YOUR BODY CAN DO.

The Body Mindset

Physical performance is physical performance. We may be at different levels, but we all have to get our heads in the place that makes us perform at our own personal best.

If your personal best is eating and performing in a way to lose the weight, then you need to get into the mindset it take to do that effectively. If you're personal best is to go to bed tonight one step closer to your goals than you were before, then you need to get into the mindset it takes to do that. One of the biggest reasons we struggle to stay on track or accomplish the goals we have for ourselves and our bodies, is we don't get into the mindset it takes to do it.

We often see ourselves as so different when we are in different physical places. Really, we're not. The top of our game may be the same, after all, the top of our game doesn't even stay the same across our own lifespan, but we must all get our heads in the place it takes to perform at it. People who are overweight, out of shape or obese are really no different than the athletes of our world in that, the place we are at in our heads determines where on our own personal scale of ability we perform. Mindset affects that edge we have with our own ability.

No matter who we are or how far we have to go, we must all get in the place it takes to be effective and reach that next level of performance for ourselves in our minds and we may need a little help with the mindset it takes to do it.

People who are not athletes need to get in the mindset for physical performance, and their best effort just as athletes do.

1.   We need to visualize ourselves being effective and living that way. We need to ourselves winning and accomplishing those goals.
2.   We need to get and stay in a mental place where we believe in our power to do it.
3.   We need to practice and rehearse each day mentally before we get up and play it.

4. We need to be in the mental place to be 'on point' or 'at the top of our game' just as athletes do.

5. And we need the resilient mindset that will help us bounce back and be in it for the long haul when it's hard.

An athlete must begin to see him or herself as a world-class athlete before he or she will do what it takes to perform and train like one. Equally, a person who is overweight, not eating right or not in the shape they want to be in must see him or herself as a person who can create his or her own amazing makeover story before he or she will put in what it takes to do it.

Our mind and our physical performance will always be inseparably connected because our minds and our bodies are.

Mentally, we must move from a place of mental weakness to a more powerful mental place in this area of our lives in our mind. We must move from seeing ourselves as a person who is flawed or unmotivated or who has little willpower, to seeing ourselves as a person who is going to get where we want to be if it is the last thing we do.

The way we see ourselves and the world around us determines who we are, what we do and how we perceive and experience our life and the things around us.

Our 'Body Mindset,' is the way we see ourselves, our ability and all the physical parts of our lives. When we see the process as hard or miserable, it will be. When we see ourselves as not competent or unable to do it, we won't be. If we think we don't have any willpower, we won't. Like the old saying goes, *"It doesn't' matter if you think you can or you can't, you're right!"*

Changing directions physically requires a mental change of direction as well. Getting on different physical track requires switching onto a different mental track in your mind. Losing weight and getting fit is not just about switching to a new daily routine of eating right and working out. It is getting into the mindset that puts you on that different physical track so you will.

One mindset results in living in a way that will make you overweight or obese. Another mindset comes with different expectations and a level of performance that will take you somewhere else.

Of course, our minds and bodies are inseparably connected. They can't even function without each other. We are integrated human beings. The way we physically live affects how we think and feel and the way we think and feel affects the way we physically live. Our minds, thoughts, actions and feelings will always affect each other because we are complex, interrelated human beings.

If we want to have the power to get where we physically want to be, we must begin to see things in ways that give us the power and determination we need to achieve our visions and goals.

Ultimately, the shape and condition of your body comes from the way you live and the way you live is determined by the way you feel about yourselves and the things around you. It only makes sense, that if you want to get effective at achieving your body goals, you MUST get your head in the place it takes to do it.

YOU CAN DO THIS

No matter what you have done in the past, you have what it takes to achieve your body goals and get your body where you want it to be. You have what it takes to do this. You just have to get your head in the place it takes to get it done.

Even if you have struggled with your body mentally or physical for years. Even if you have been in a slump, you've given up or you've been mentally and physically sliding in the wrong direction for years, get in a different place in your mind, get on a different mental and physical track and you will.

You have what it takes to get on track with your body and your physical goals. I know what it feels like to think that you can't, and I know what it feels like when you flip that mental switch in your head that says, "I can and I will, and I'm done going in that direction."

Literally, I can feel when I mentally switch into that competent place in my head. Sadly, it took me decades to find out that I even had one. I hope to save you that time and pain by telling you that you can get into a more competent physical place in your head. We all can. In many ways, we perform and feel like the person we physically think ourselves to be. You don't have to let yourself be incompetent or weak in this area. Your Body Mindset, like any other, is a choice. Make the decision to do it. Get into the mental place that give you the power and resilience to accomplish this goal and you will find ability you didn't know you had.

In EVERY area of life, mindset RADICALLY CHANGES the person you are and the things you get out of you. Find mindset it takes to live your life in a body you are happy to be in. This book (along with some coaching if you need it) will help you get there. NOTE: YOU CAN DOWNLOAD A FREE WORKBOOK FOR THIS JOURNEY BY VISITING US AT OUR WEBSITE WWW.THEBODYMINDSETBOOK.COM

'OUT OF THE PARK MINDSET'

One of the most powerful and effective mindsets you can get yourself into is one I like to call your 'Out of the Park Mindset.'

In baseball, when a batter steps up to the place, his or her belief that he will hit that ball out of the park, determines the way he or she swings at that ball.

Your belief that you are going to be effective at something, determines the way you mentally and physically approach that thing. Getting into an 'Out of the Park Mindset' with your body goals radically determines the effectiveness you have with it.

With the belief that you will step up to the diet or fitness plate and dramatically change the way your body is with what you do, you approach that goal completely differently than you do when you think, 'I'll try' or 'as long as it's not too hard.'

Reaching that, 'I'm going to hit this 'Out of the Park' place with your body goal translates to a completely different level of decisiveness and determination to do it.

One of the things that makes an 'Out of the Park' mindset so powerful is that changes the percentage of your ability you put into that swing. As a kid, I never believed I would hit the ball. In fact, I would have been surprised if I did. There was no force or follow through in my swing because I was pretty sure I would fail. That is the mental way that many of us step up to the plate with our body goals, if we do it at all. Instead, we must step up to that body goal in the mindset it takes to really hit this body goal 'Out of Park.' We must get in the mental place to make a major change to our bodies in a big way, and the determination to stick with this attempt until we do.

Instead, we don't realize we do this, but we step up to that goals hopeful that this time it will be easier, or we will be stronger, but we step up to that place hoping we will get lucky and 'win the body lottery.' We mentally hope, but as we do, we step up to our body goals with the full intention of failing.

We want to get 'lucky' but mentally we don't swing at our body goal like we are in it to win it. Mentally, we go in kicking and screaming and dragging our feet, hoping it won't be hard or take long and wishing we didn't have to it.

We build in an 'out clause' we can use if things get too hard. We mentally get in the game 'as long as' we are feel like it, we are not too tired or something else in life doesn't get in the way.

We go in knowing that 'if we feel too hungry' or 'if we can't handle it' or 'if something comes up' we are going to be so out of there.

Instead of stepping up to the plate to hit that body goal 'Out of the Park' we swing like I did when my main goal was to use that bat to keep the ball from hitting me.

Most of don't' realize how many mental outs we plan into our commitment to pursue our body goal.

THAT 'OUT OF THE PARK' PLACE

This time, when you begin your physical goal, do so with the absolute intention of creating dramatic success with the makeover of body goal. Getting in the mindset to be wildly successful with this body goal and hit this thing 'Out of the Park' will dramatically change the way you do it.

Few of us realize that we mentally swing at our body goals with as much fear and lack of belief as we do. We don't realize that mentally we don't get 'In it to Win it' or that we mentally build so many exits in to let ourselves out if it gets too hard.

I remember the day I mentally got into a different place with my body for the first time. I had tried hundreds of diets in my life without much success. When I finally mentally said, "I am not going that direction again. I don't care what it takes. I don't' care if this is going to be hard or I'm going to need to get hungry. I don't' care if I have to eat less than others or workout more. I WILL MAKE THIS HAPPEN and I don't care what it takes." When I mentally got in the to win it, I stepped up to that place in a way I never physically did before.

When I stepped up to the body change plate with the full intention that I was going to hit this thing 'Out of the Park' I quit caring if it was going to be hard or I was going to be tired. I completely quit caring if I was going to miss out on cake. For the first time in my life, I cared about ONE THING. I quit caring about if it was going to be hard, or what I might have to give up and started caring about only one thing, what would it take to be effective?

When I mentally took away the option to fail, and got in it to win it, I quit caring about the cost or what I might feel or if it would be hard. When I get determined to do it in the right way, I knew I was approaching this goal in a way I never had before. When I stepped up to the plate with my body goal with the full intention that I would put EVERYTHING I mentally and physically had into my attempt to do it without holding anything back I did. When I stepped up to the place with the full intention of getting where I wanted to be, I did!

Perhaps, you too haven't yet made your own dramatic body transformation the way you wanted to, because you never stepped up the plate with the full intention to hit this body goal 'Out of the Park' and get where you want to be at all cost.

Perhaps, no matter how many times you have tried, you never fully got 'In It to Win It' in your mind so you could.

GET 'ON POINT' IN YOUR MIND

When you get 'In It to Win It' with your body goal, you live your day in a different way. Instead of living on excuses, your excuses mean nothing to you. In the right mindset, we could care less if there are reasons not to. In the right mindset, the cost doesn't matter. When you hit 'THE TIPPING POINT' of commitment and determination it takes to do this, you will go 'all in' in what you are willing to put in to make it happen. When you do, you begin getting 'On Point' and strategic about the execution of that goal.

When I finally got in it to win it, I woke up, mentally reviewed my day, and then performed that day 'on point.' When I get determined to win it, the way I attacked that body goal was NOTHING LIKE the way I did before. When I got 'In It to Win It' I got 'On Point' with the way I did my day. I didn't eat snacks. I ate what I planned when I planned to eat it and I didn't let myself even consider not doing that.

I quit suffering over the alternative because I quit mentally considering them. I made a plan and performed that daily plan, 'On Point' the way I planned it. When it quit working, or I fell down in my execution, I saw that as knowledge that I could use to prevent that failure again or modify the plan. When I got mentally 'IN IT TO WIN IT' I got strategic in a way that took away all that mental struggle I had before. I had a daily goal. I made a daily plan, and I performed the details of my eating and working out plan to perfection.

GETTING IN 'IT TO WIN IT'

When you really step up to the plate with the full intention of doing this, not matter what, it changes the game in how you feel and what you do. When you are in this to win it, and you go to bed knowing you performed on point, you lie in bed with pride knowing you 'NAILED IT!' It mentally feels good to be completely in on a goal that you make, and the power and emotion you get from that ripples out into the rest of your life when you do.
When you make a NO EXCUSES COMMITMENT to get somewhere in your life and you mentally get in the place it takes to ACCEPT THE COST and allow nothing less from yourself until you do, you quit trying and start doing.

For literally decades of my life, I thought I was doing the best that I could with myself and my body. I thought I was trying.

Little did I know I was playing my body game the same way I would swing at the ball in baseball. I was holding something back. Actually, I was holding everything back. I swung at my body goal enough to make myself think I tried, but instead, I PROVED to myself that I couldn't, just like I did in baseball.

Get 'Into It to 'Win It' make you step up to that goal with a MINDSET OF SUCCESS. Getting into your body goal with full intention and determination to make a dramatic change to your body makes you step up to that goal with the full intention of hitting it 'Out of the Park.'

You may have tried unsuccessfully for a lifetime, like I did, but when you finally step up to this goal with the determination to put everything you have into that swing it will change the game for you, just like it did for me. Step up to the plate with full determination to hit this 'Out of the Park' and you will refuse to back down or give up until you do.

HOW DOES YOUR MINDSET AFFECT YOUR EATING?

In the wrong mindset, we allow far too many 'reasons' and 'excuses' not to. We EXCUSE ourselves from eating right because today was hard, or we don't feel like it today. In the wrong mindset, we see our excuses as reasons, and we are always bargaining with some reason not to. In the wrong mindset, we can't keep our eyes off the cake on the counter and we keep considering all those justifications and 'reasons' we have for letting ourselves eat a little bit of it. In the wrong mindset we FLIRT WITH FAILURE and keep temptation on our mind.
The same thing is true of fitness. When you are not mentally in it to win it, NOT DOING IT IS ALWAYS AN OPTION, so is eating wrong. If we can mentally justify eating badly or not working out, we will. In the wrong mindset we are fishing for a reason to let ourselves justify not doing this today and if that means feeling bad for ourselves or being miserable to let ourselves out, we will.

In a self-sabotage place, we keep looking at, thinking about, and considering the alternative. In the wrong mental place, we seem to want an excuse that gives us reason not to. Take away the option to fail or the option to eat that cake or not work out, and actually doing it is FAR EASIER than it is when we don't.

It turns out that all that THE BATTLE THAT MAKES STAYING ON TRACK SO HARD takes place in our heads. Staying on track with our body goals is only hard because we keep considering and trying to talk ourselves out of the alternative. Once we would quit flirting with and considering temptation, staying on the right track with something in our lives is far easier than we thought.

It is easy to convince yourself you have a hundred different reasons to fail. It is also easy to convince yourself life did that and it's not your fault. All that is just falling for a victim mentality that makes it easier to justify failure. You might have a hundred reasons life is hard that you could us to justify failure, but when you get IN IT TO WIN IT, you no longer care.

Take away the option to fail and quit considering the alternative to doing it and it will far easier than you thought it could be.

Most of us don't ever experience our physical limits because we get stopped by our mental limits long before we get there. Did your body reach a place where it could no longer handle that hunger, or that workout, or did you mentally cave long before you got there? Make all your limits be real. *The place to stop is where your body says it is, not where your head does.*

ON THE FLIP SIDE

An effective mindset is its own kind of high. Few of us realize how good it feels to be on track and be really effective at moving toward where we want to be. Being effective with our bodies may be hard, but it is its own kind of high.

Most of us know how painful and debilitating it can be to be going in the wrong direction physically and to feel powerless to stop that slide that we're in. Mentally and physically, it feels terrible to be going in the wrong direction. Well, the flip side of that is that it feels empowering and amazing to know that we are in charge and going int eh right direction. It feels exhilarating to be in charge of where you are going and be moving in the direction it takes to get there.

Many of us who struggle with our bodies never know how good it feels to be on the other track. We fear it. We are afraid it will be hard or that we will feel hunger or our heartbeat.

We know we hate the debilitating mindsets of ineffectiveness. We hate that we feel stuck or powerless. Those of us who have been stuck there know the very real pain, frustration, hate and self-loathing that comes on the flip side of going in right direction, yet we fear it will hurt when we do.

In all reality, everything we want to feel is right on the other side. We fear what we think we will feel. Really, everything we want and need to feel comes from getting in that powerful and positive Body Mindset and being on track with our visions and our goals.

The spiral of negative emotion and direction that hurt our bodies, hurt us far deeper than that. On the flip side of that right mindset is all our pain. On the flip side of the right Body Mindset is the place where we mental screw it up and beat ourselves up when we do. That place is horrible! We fear what we don't know, but the right direction is where things feel the way they should.

When you are on the wrong side of your Body Mindset, you can't seem to pull it together even though you feel frustrated and mad at yourself that you can't. As you fear the physical part of changing your body know that pain is nothing to feeling powerless or being 'not enough' in your head.

Those of us who have been in the wrong place or going in the wrong physical direction need to recognize that is a mental breath of fresh air to get back on track with our bodies. Our worst pain is not having that craving or missing that food or feeling your heartbeat. The worst pain of our lives is those frustrating, painful, and debilitating places where we are not enough, or can't do something right in our minds.

EVERYTHING YOU WANT WITH YOUR BODY

IS ON THE OTHER SIDE OF THE FEAR

YOU HAVE OF DOING IT.

Even when you are one track, it is important to recognize when your thoughts and feelings are starting to slip so you can fix it. Spirals in thought and behavior feed each other. Recognize when you are slipping in both thought and behavior so you can mentally get yourself back on the powerful side of you.

Here are some warning signs that you are falling into that unproductive and painful Body Mindset.

- You start listening to and believing your own excuses.
- You start feeling sorry for yourselves.
- You logic and excuse your way out of things.
- You kill your progress with one-time exceptions to your own rules.
- You start taking two steps forward and three steps back and you aren't getting anywhere significantly better at all.

In the wrong mindset, your problems are huge, your resources are small, and you feel that you are not good at this and whatever you do will be less than enough.

- In the wrong mindset, you get stuck.
- You procrastinate everything you want away because there always seem to be a better and easier time that will have less struggle to do it later.
- In the wrong mindset, you are powerless, and it is not your fault. Life and genetics stack together against you and you get resigned to give up because you can't do anything about it anyway. In fact, you have proof you can't because you've 'tried.'
- In the wrong mindset, you incorrectly believe a lot of de-powering things about yourself and your ability to do something better with your body. You might believe it is because of your genetics, or your willpower, or all the problems in your life you didn't plan.
- When we believe things that take away our power, they make us think we can't. and that affects our effort and ability.
- In addition, perhaps the worst of all the negative places to be is the one that causes is to get into that mental and physical spiral of doom where we are going down on a crash and burn course to our destruction. The struggles we have with our body goals, originate from a mindset.

When you recognize elements of the wrong mindset in yourself, stop yourself. Give yourself a Mindset Makeover and get yourself back into the mental place where you can, and you will!

THE TIPPING POINT OF DETERMINATION

Few of us access the full extent of our ability to do anything. In fact, there are a variety of factors that give us access to more or less of the ability that we actually have factors like lack of commitment, priority, and belief, give a low access to the ability we actually have, while determination and belief let us tap into more of the innate ability to do things we have inside.

The priority we place on something greatly changes how much of our own ability we get to access when we do it. The determination we have to do something makes us much more effective at doing it. Sadly, the reason some of us think we don't have much ability, is we never really get into the mindset to access much of the actual ability we have.

Often, the reason we can't is we don't get in the mental place it takes to find out what physical or mental ability to do this is in there when we dig deep enough to find it. When we do, dig deep enough, we often find we have more physical and mental power and ability than we thought we did. We rarely reach real limits to the ability of what we can physically do, because our minds shut us down long before we get there. In most things that we do, we rarely access all the ability we have. The factor that gives us access to the highest percentage of our ability is determination.

With the right level of determination to do something we access FAR closer to 100% of our own ability. When we get into our place of mental strength and reach the **Tipping Point of Determination** to get something done, and you find a way to do it.

The reason we often think we don't have the ability to do something, like lose weight, or stick with an eating plan we didn't know we could master is often because we are not yet mentally committed enough to do it. Until we reach that **tipping point of the determination** it takes to do something well, we won't be able to successfully access enough of the ability we have to do it. Sometimes our belief and determination to do something are so low, that we don't even realize we have it in us.

DETERMINATION

When we reach the right level of determination to do something, we get access to close to 100% of the ability we have to do it. Get determined enough to do it, and we don't care if it is challenging or will take a long time for us to do. With the right level of determination, we get committed to not let anything stop us or get in the way and we don't pull out that challenge just because it's hard. Reach the tipping point of determination it takes to do something, and you get access to nearly 100% of the ability you have to do it.

Reach that, **'Stand Back and Watch Me'** or **'I'll do this or die trying'** place in our minds and it gets far easier to do. The challenge we thought was inherent in something that is hard to do is often caused by us dragging our feet and not putting in much of the effort we have. Get 100% committed to do something and you get access to a magical amount of ability you didn't know you had.

Determination removes barriers and irradicates excuse. When you are not completely committed you break easily and think you don't have the ability it takes to do it. Get determined enough to do something and you will find ability to do it you didn't know you had.

There is a Tipping Point of Determination in your own mind that it will take to change the game and ultimately your success with this body goal. Get determined enough to do it and you won't quit until you do. How determined are you to accomplish this body goal?

Get determined enough to do something that you don't care what it takes and your will. It is your determination and resilience that will change the game and make you effective at losing weight or getting into a shape you love.

Babe Ruth is famous from saying,

"YOU CAN'T BEAT A PERSON WHO JUST WON'T QUIT."

Make the right kind of no failure option decision to do this and you'll find you have more willpower and physical ability than you thought. Get determined enough to make it happen and you will get resilient enough to not quit until you figure it out and find a way. Get omitted enough to doing this and you will find that you have far more ability to do this than you thought you did.

Raise your expectations and take away failure as an option in your mind. Get more determined to do it, and you will demand and find a higher level of ability in yourself.

When you make the right kind of commitment, you dig a little deeper, or a lot deeper into the ability you have, and you find out what you really can do. When you reach **the tipping point of determination** it takes to make this happen, you find that you have the resilience, effectiveness, and physical and mental ability to make it happen.

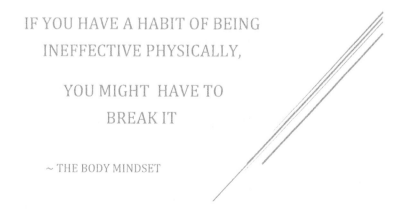

IF YOU HAVE A HABIT OF BEING
INEFFECTIVE PHYSICALLY,

YOU MIGHT HAVE TO
BREAK IT

~ THE BODY MINDSET

Overview of the

Body Mindset Process

This book is structured into three parts.

1. BODY MINDSET PRINCIPLES

2. THE BODY MINDSET RETREAT

3. TIME FOR CLARITY AND PLANNING

At the heart of this book is a Body Mindset Retreat. This retreat is a time to personally focus and commit to your body goals so you can get your head in the place to successfully achieve those goals.

While a Body Mindset Retreat is not required, it can significantly change the direction you are going. It can help move you towards a different mental and physical track.

A typical one-day retreat is from 6 to 8 hours, alone, and in the privacy of your own home. This is a time to mentally tie into your strength, make the commitments, and plan for what it takes to change directions in your physical life. If you can't do a one-day retreat, you can break it up into smaller sections to make it better fit your life. A Mindset Retreat puts you on a new track so you can get yourself there physically.

If you would like to do a Mindset Retreat, here are some things to help you prepare:

1. Schedule a day for it. Take some time off or arrange to be alone for 6 to 8 hours to focus on getting into your goal mindset.

2. Anticipate the day. A Mindset Retreat is like a day at a luxurious day spa that will put you back in control of your body and give you direction. For many of us, a Body Mindset Retreat is just what we need. It is restful, invigorating, and enjoyable. Schedule your retreat and then look forward to it as you would a much-needed vacation.

3. Read the book. As you wait, read the book, and learn all you can about mindset so you will be ready to make a new commitment to this goal.

4. When the day of your retreat arrives, read Part Two of this book, but also set the book aside from time to time to reflect and write as you go.

5. ENJOY IT! The more enjoyable and memorable you make this DAY, the more of a change agent it will be in your life. Let yourself enjoy this much needed mental and physical retreat.

6. End with time for clarity and planning. This is where you will clarify the plans and routines needed to make this goal fit into your life. Be sure to disaster proof your goal by predicting problems and plans to prevent them.

   Finally, get physically ready. Shop for the food, lay out your fitness clothes, remove the junk food from your house, etc.

   By the end of the day, you should be:

a. Mentally committed.
b. Clear about what you will do and how it will look in your daily life.
c. Physically prepared with the food and supplies you need to get up and get going without struggle in the morning.

   A Mindset Retreat is the mental and physical preparation it takes to successfully achieve your goals. It is priming the pump for your fitness or weight loss success.

POWERFUL SELF-TALK

The words we say to ourselves in our own minds are perhaps the most important element of the success in EVERYTHING WE DO.

As a pre-teen, I read a book that stuck with me for the rest of my life. That book was about the power of SELF-TALK. It was my first awareness that the thoughts I said to myself in my head determined my emotion and the things I did in my life. As a girl in perhaps upper elementary, I highlighted the book and wrote in the margins of a book for the first time in my life. That book made such a big impression on me, that it became part of the way I have lived my life.

Sadly, I didn't make the same self-talk connection with my body goals. We must become our own coaches and cheerleaders in our body goals as well. We must ALWAYS talk to ourselves in ways that give us the power and energy and motivation to do the things that we do. Our self-talk sets and sustains our drive and our motivation to do things. It is the way that we talk to and support ourselves in our own minds that motivate us and give us the mental power and mental vibe it takes to get it done.

We must begin to talk to ourselves in our minds in ways that give us the power and drive we need to achieve our physical goals. It is the words we say to ourselves that creates our vibe and our drive.

We must mentally generate the energy, and confidence and drive it takes to get where we want to be in our heads, and we must use the energy and contents of our own thoughts to sustain our efforts and keep ourself in the mental place it take to get there. In addition, our self-talk generates our emotion and our emotional vibe. The energy we surround ourselves with and allow to flow through us powers and sustains the things that we do. We get the power to do the things that we do from the power we allow to throw threw us.

Become aware of your own self talk. Is it kind? Is it motivating? Is it building up you and your abilities, or is your self-talk tearing you down? Mentally talk yourself into success in your head.

BECOME A FRIEND AND A COACH TO YOURSELF

One of the best things you will ever do for yourself in every way is to become a friend and coach for yourself in your head. Let the self-talk you have going on in your head be the self-talk you need to hear.
Notice when your self-talk is tearing you down and making you miserable or ineffective. When your self-talk becomes unsupportive or hurtful or dis-powering shut it down immediately and change the channel on your thoughts. Use that constant stream of self-talk you have going on in your head to become the coach, friend, and support system you need for success and happiness in your life. Step by step, mentally talk your way through getting better with your body. Supportively talk yourself successfully through this day. Use your self-talk as a powerful tool in your body goals and it will be like you have the friends and coach you need with you all the time in your mind.

Your self-talk is more valuable that you will ever know. Monitor your self-talk and become aware of the words you are saying to yourself in your head. Then the words you say to yourself in your head, be the ones you need to hear in your mind and your life.

Become a coach and friend to yourself in your mind. Every day guides yourself toward success at your goals that day with the best and most supportive kind of self-talk you could have toward yourself in your mind.
Like good parent would raise a child, use a nearly constant stream of love, guidance, support, celebration, and encouragement to raise yourself from where you are and coach, guide and encourage yourself through every step of each day as you slowly get stronger and better and closer and toward where you want to be.

CELEBRATE THE HECK OUT OF YOUR PROGRESS INSIDE AS YOU GO!

One element of self-talk is perhaps more powerful than any other and that is emotionally rewarding every step you take in the right direction as you take it.

Your self-talk can powerfully talk you out of doing things you shouldn't do, but even more valuable is the power of praising the heck out of yourself whenever you do right, you use your willpower, you make a good food choice, you walk past a bad one, or you take a step in the right direction. The more you use your self-talk to reward the right things, the more progress you make in the right direction.

As everyone who knows about behavior control knows, you get more of what you focus on and reward. The more you praise your success, progress, and good decisions, the more of them you are going to get out of yourself. You need to mentally reward your behavior to increase it, just as you may physically and emotionally reward the behavior of you kids when they do the right things so you will get more of that.

Good self-talk is being a parent, a coach and best friend to yourself. Just as we parent our kids by encouraging, rewarding and celebrating who they are and what they do right, we must use our own self-talk to parent and coach and encourage ourselves. Our own supportive and motivating self-talk is one the most powerful tools we have to make us successful at achieving our body goals. Become the friend, coach and support system you need on this journey with the words you say to yourself in the privacy of your own head.

My first experience with mindset or that awareness of my own thoughts they called metacognition was probably in that book about self-talk I read as a young adolescent.

I became a believer in mindset the moment I read that book and tried the concepts of it on myself. I suddenly became more conscious of the way I was talking to myself in my head and handled my life mentally.

I noticed the way my own self talk changed the way I felt and the power I had to do things. I became aware that the way I interpreted and framed things in my mind dramatically affected me and my performance. I had to believe in my ability to accomplish and figure things out in my mind, and use my self-talk to build and support the faith I had in myself to physically accomplish this goal.

Even years after I recognized the power of self-talk, I didn't apply that to my body or body goals. I believe in mindset, and knew the importance of self-talk, yet it took decades for me to connect the dots and realize that I also had to apply these mental skills and change the way I saw myself and my physical ability to reach my goal physically.

I converted to the power of mindset in my life, my job, my education, my life as a parent, long before I saw that I also had to change the way I saw things and talked to myself in my mind about my body and living healthy. I don't know why, but it eluded me that I had to get into a more powerful and determined place in my head and better mindset skills physically if I was every going to get more effective with my body.

One day, when I was struggling with what seemed to be my own incompetence at this, I had an interesting thought. What if the reason I seemed to be so incompetent in my physical life is simply because I let myself feel that way? What if the only reason I was spinning my wheels and fighting my motivation the way I was I was letting myself be 'not enough' physically in my head? What if all this tendency I had to struggle and procrastinate with my body goals just a place I was letting myself be in my head?

What if all this struggle I seemed to have with my willpower and motivation and the way I was living my life physically was just a self-fulfilling prophecy because I didn't believe in myself and my ability to do it?

WHAT IF IT IS JUST A MINDSET?

It was a radical thought for me to finally realize that the ONLY reason I couldn't do is was I was not in the right mental place to do it right or do it well. For years I had wondered what was wrong with me. Why did my willpower and motivation seem lower than others? Why did it seem like I couldn't do it? What was wrong with me, or what skill was I missing that others seemed to have. Was it genetic? Was it a product of my life, my upbringing or perhaps a personal deficit in me or the willpower I was born with?

This new belief that perhaps, it was all just a completely changeable mindset was empowering. If I had just not been in the right mental place in my life, I could change that! Mindset gave me power in the body game, just as it did in EVERY other area of my life. I worked on improving both my behavior and my mindset.

I worked on changing the way I saw myself, and the process. I worked on not seeing it as harder than it is. I worked on seeing it as a joy and a quality-of-life choice, instead of just another 'should.' Most of all, I worked on my own determination and seeing my way to through today as well as crossing that finish line of that goal in my mind. I worked on not catastrophizing the process or my own life and I worked on seeing myself as the healthy and fit person who lived the life it takes to get there in my mind.

In short, all the diets and fitness and weight loss in the world never got me anywhere until I combined those things with the mindset it took to do them effectively. When I did, I got effective at losing nearly a hundred pounds, got active, and I learned to love it. A lot of surprising things happened when I combined the right routine with the mindset it takes to do it. When I did, the boost of power and confidence I got from it radiated into other parts of my life as well. A better Body Mindset, like all our mindset skills, radiates strength and joy and confidence into the way you live your life physically, just as it does into the rest of your life as well.

Getting into a better Body Mindset changed the way I live my physical life, It took away all that artificial difficultly I was building into it in my mind.

The right mindset makes it easier, or even enjoyable to do. There is a mindset that will make you effective at the body goals you have. Find it and you will get successful at accomplishing things you never thought you could.

You can do this! You just need to get into the mindset it takes to get effective at getting the body and performance you want.

Mindset and self-talk are incredibly powerful
because the talk you allow in your mind changes
everything about the person you are
and the experiences you have!

You have the power to do this. You always have.

You simply must get into the mindset it takes to make

you effective at achieving your body goals!

There is nothing more powerful than your state of your mind! Get converted to the power of mindset in your life! Learn it, live it, and believe it. Mindset gives you power over yourself, your emotion, and your skill. It lets you find your own power even in circumstances you can't control. Your choice of your own mindset makes you powerful and effective in many areas of life. Learn to use the choice you have of your own perception, belief, and frame of mind to make you feel the way you want to feel and be the way you want to be.

Because mindset is so powerful, it can dramatically change your body, just as it changes you and your effectiveness and experience in every other area of your life. Mindset puts you together and makes you powerful and effective, or it tears you apart and destroy both you and your confidence.

GET IN THE .MINDSET THAT
WILL GIVE YOU THE POWER
TO HAVE THE LIFE AND
BODY YOU WANT TO HAVE!

MY VISION

As a writer, I believe in throwing my dreams out there to my readers because I believe there is always someone out there with the power to hear them and make them come true, so here goes.

First, I believe that many of my struggles with my body, or at least the most painful part of them started with PE in junior high. I think we do a terrible job with the kids who are most at risk of becoming obese adults when we throw them all into one-size fits all programs where they are forced to perform at levels above their physical ability in front of their more fit and able peers.

Just at the time kids are most socially vulnerable, and y want to fit in, we make them perform and compete in front of everyone else. I came out of that feel this I was not competent, and not physically like everyone else. Worst of all, I came out feel like I HATED IT.

I think we are actually making things FAR WORSE for our kids who are most physically vulnerable with the physical education programs we have in schools now.

My first vision is that we revamp the physical educations programs because, by the look of society, they are obviously NOT EFFECTIVE at what they were intended to do.

In education, we believe success for all happens by having Tier 1, Tier 2 and 3 programs. This means that most kids are served well with whole group education. Another part of them will also need smaller group remediation, and others may need help that is more individual and tailored to where they are.

> Why do we still have one-size fits all physical education programs, when we don't have one-size fits all kids?

My first vision is that we restructure our physical education programs in school, not completely, (although even our mainstream kids need to be taught how to eat and think right.) I think all PE programs need some classroom instruction about mindset.

Mostly, however, I think we need to add Tier 2 and 3 programs to our schools to serve the needs of all our physically diverse students. In my dream, this includes fun success and enjoyment-based physical programs in Tier 2 groups that are more at these students physical and levels so they learn that they can and even more importantly, that they can enjoy physical activity.

We also need Tier 3 groups for our kids who are already obese or at high-risk of it based on risk factors at home. Tier 3 physical education would consist of personal coaching where kids could sit down with someone, perhaps a school nutritionist, and make some personal physical goals. As part of this they would receive instruction on how to cook healthy food. They would get to try it. They would get instruction in Body Mindset, success-based goals (which are not the way obese people think they have to lose weight. Based on my family and the people I've worked with, obese people think they need to starve themselves and run 20 miles a day to be different.

The OBESE MINDSET is to psych yourself out by thinking you have to do something so extreme that you know you can't do it. They get desperate and try, then fail, and PROVE ONE AGAIN TO THEMSLEVES THAT THEY CAN'T. I know that mindset, and many of the kids who grow up with that modeled for them at home NEVER see another option for how to look at it. An obese mindset is learned at home and for many of our kids, this, combined with the incompetence and comparison the programs we put them in school make them feel, nearly insure they will become the obese adults of tomorrow.

With the right physical programs in school, I think we can really make some progress at solving obesity in the future. IF THE MINDSET OF OBESITY AND A FEELING OF PHYSICAL INCOMPETNCE ARE THE ROOT CAUSES OF OBESITY, THEN THE ONLY WAY WE ARE GOING TO AFFECT THE HEALTH OF THESE KIDS IN THE FUTURE IS TO TEACH, NOT JUST A WAY TO EAT, BUT THE WAYS TO THINK AND FEEL THAT WILL CHANGE THAT IN THE FUTURE.

Kids who are most at risk of obesity need to learn that they can and that they can love it. They need to experience success! Our real goal of physical education needs to be like our real goal of education, which is to create life-long learners. Our goal of physical education can't just be to build some temporary muscles now. We MUST create programs, that will change the way kids feel about themselves and the process that will affect their ability and desire to be LIFE-LONG HEALTHY ADULTS.

And sense I'm at it, here is my other one. This should probably be left for another book because it involves business, but I think our adult population would be healthier and happier if we build some time for mindset into the workplace as well. This is how I see it happening.

First, since taking care of our health requires us to get into the mindset to make that happen, I think businesses should see the value of Mindset Retreats for employees.

Employees need time and space to get into the mindset they need to be healthy. They also need some planned time to get into the mindset it takes for corporate changes or to be effective at work. Part of a 'sharpen the saw' mentally could be to give employees one planned day per year to get into the mindset they need to take care of their bodies and personal directions the way that they should.

This could be done at work or at home. I believe that Mindset Retreats for employees could help them get into the mindset to accomplish their own physical and even their corporate goals.

Giving employees one day a year dedicated to their own Body Mindset could more than pay for itself in improved health, happiness and attendance and that improved health might even lower a company's health risk and cost of insurance.

By giving employees time at work to get into the mindset to corporate goals or to get in the mindset it takes to be effective at work, and time once a year at home or at work to get into the place to better take care of their health and their bodies, I think corporation could improve the mental and physical health of the employees they have.

I even see more objective specific Mindset Retreats for teams that are focused on a specific objective. Here they could spend a part of the day on the vision of the project and the mindset of success and another part of the day on the plan it takes to get there.

Since the mindset to do it is a prerequisite for ALL KINDS OF SUCCESS, and getting into that OUT OF THE PARK mindset changes the ability we have to accomplish our lofty goals, then getting into that mindset MUST BE A PRIORITY for business, just as it is for individuals who must get their heads in that place to build that climate of success in themselves.

By giving employees time to wrap their heads around their personal and professional goals, companies could affect the health, happiness and success of their employees as well.

Of course, that is better left for another book, but the idea that mindset and Mindset Retreats are powerful for far more than body goals, is a vision of mine and since I believe that throwing your visions out there, is the best way to reach the people with the power it takes to do them, I decide to put these two visions I have in this book as well.

If anyone would like to hear more of my ideas in these areas, I have them, and would be glad to share if anyone is interested in picking up the dreams that I am throwing out for someone to see.

SET PRIORITY AND ESTABLISH DIRECTION

It is time for all of those of us who are here to improve our bodies to schedule and get ready for our Mindset Retreats.

Of course you can lose weight or get fit without one, but you do need time to mentally change direction no matter how you decide to do it.

A Mindset Retreat is a time for you personally GET OFF THE TREADMILL OF LIFE for long enough to decide what matters and get your head in the place it takes to go there. It is the time to get effective and powerful mentally so you can , get effective, change the direction you are going physically and get effective with your body goals.

Besides a Mindset Retreat is just plain FUN! Even at home by yourself, your retreat is a mini vacation for your body and mind. It is a time to pamper, think, experience peace and joy and the luxury of feeling physically and emotionally the way that you should.

Whether you choose a retreat or not, pamper and get back on track mentally as you read this book. Taking care of yourself physically and mentally sends the message that you can and you're worth it. Relax, get your mind back in the right place and enjoy the restfulness of your I highly recommend that you consider taking a day or two to get your head in the weight loss or fitness game so you will be mentally and physically ready to take your body in a new direction.

REMEMBER: SHAELEE AND I ALSO OFFER WEEKEND AND 3-DAY RETREATS GUIDED BODY-MINDSET RETREATS THAT WILL GET YOU MENTALLY AND PHYSICALLY BACK ON TRACK AS WELL. SIGN UP AND JOIN US FOR A RETREAT HERE IN UTAH IF YOU CAN.

HOW TO PREPARE FOR YOUR RETREAT

If you are doing your own retreat, there are a few things you need to do in advance to prepare:

1. Time — A Mindset Retreat requires some planning.

    To get ready for your retreat, you need to schedule a time and place to make it happen. Schedule 6 to 8 hours of uninterrupted time where you can be quiet, be alone, and have the time to focus.

2. Supplies — Having some personal care items on hand can make your retreat more memorable and enjoyable and, therefore, make it a more powerful element of change in your life.

    Consider having skin and body care items you enjoy, a bath bomb, ex-foliation products, hair and nail care items, aromatherapy, candles and/or music if you desire. None of these items are required, so add anything that is meaningful or relaxing for you. This is your day. Prepare to enjoy it!

3. Silence — Since clarity and mindset are the main objectives, quiet and serenity are essential. If it is impossible to create a quiet space during the day, you may want to get up early or spend some time alone after you put the kids to bed at night. Just ensure you have some quiet, uninterrupted time alone to think.

4. Paper — Another thing you may want to bring is a notebook or a journal so you can write down the ideas you have, plans that you make, and any other insight you have that day that could help you later.

STOP

Take a minute now to schedule your Body Mindset Retreat (the time you will get mentally in tune and on track with your body goals.)

For this retreat you will need at least six to eight hours of time alone and away from all distraction.

Now is a good time to pencil in some time to get yourself and your body back on track both mentally and physically.

save the date

Taking a day off for you is a small cost to pay to get on a new path with your body. You deserve a day for you! After you schedule your retreat, read the chapters ahead so you will be ready for that day.

THE KEY TO BEHAVIOR IS SIMPLE

YOU GET MORE OF WHAT YOU

REWARD AND EXPECT, EVEN

WITH YOURSELF

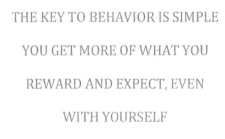

The Body Mindset

CHAPTER
TWO

THE SCIENCE
OF MINDSET

Once you understand that everything is energy, you

understand that everything you think, believe, or feel

consists of energy (it alters) your physical circumstance.

~Bentinho Massaro

Our minds and bodies will always be inseparably connected and with our increasing knowledge and technology, we are beginning to watch the science of belief move out of the realm of pseudo-science and into the realm of concrete, empirical science we can see, measure, and prove.

As technology increased to the point that we can 'see' brain activity and detect and measure the chemical messages that are created in our thoughts based on thought, we are gaining, indisputable proof that our thoughts matter. And really do change the chemical and electrical atmosphere of both our brains and our bodies.

Slowly, we are starting to look at the science of thought as a real and empirical science that dramatically impacts our body in predictable and physical ways.

For years, we have separated the 'hard sciences' of the body and the 'soft science' of thought in our mind and even the universities that study them to the point that we have failed to recognize the synergistic power of thought on chemistry and the state of our bodies on our thought. We have separated body and mind so completely in our heads that we have failed to see power of the interaction between them.

THE SCIENCE OF BELIEF

The best medicine for anything is undeniably, the right combination of healthy food, medicine, activity and thought. Despite the undeniable connection of body and mind, all previous attempt to treat or affect the human body with belief or thought intervention was automatically dismissed as pseudo-science, and for good reason.

To pass the scrutiny of science, the things we do must be empirically verifiable and reproducible by others.

For years, scientist dismissed all proposed healing properties of thought or mind as pseudo-science. Of course, real science must be held to the highest standards of empirical proof, so without the advances in technology that allow us to better 'see' what is going on in the body, the impact of our thoughts and beliefs were dismissed, and with them all opportunity to find the optimal synergistic intersection of mind and biology when they work the way they do best, together.

However, we have indisputable evidence that our thoughts and interpretations do dramatically impact the electrical and chemical states of our bodies.

Scientists who realized that the state of our minds affected some rudimentary things we could measure like the three indicators of autonomic arousal, heart rate/blood pressure, respiration, and skin conductivity, use this connection between a thought we think and the changes that causes in the things we can measures to create of the lie detector test.

You don't even need science to tell you that your thoughts affect your body. See a cop's lights in your rear-view mirror and your heart leaps into your throat. See someone suspiciously dressed and your heart pounds and the hairs on your arms stand on end. Remember that tonight is Halloween, and you laugh at yourself and go on with your day. When your brain interpreted that guy as a risk, you one interaction. When it saw a good and harmless cause for that unexpected behavior, it may have taken a few minutes, but your body reactions settled right down.

Initially we dismissed all therapeutic interaction between mind and body because we couldn't measure, see, and understand what was going on at a biological level in response to that thought. Intuitively and we know the way our bodies react that the way we interpret a situation triggers a biological response, but scientifically we had to dismiss the power of thought and belief to a fault because we couldn't measure it and didn't have the technology to see what was going on.

THE PLACEBO EFFECT

One reaction researchers dismissed mindset was that it developed a bad name when it was first recognized that belief caused 'the placebo effect.' The placebo effect was nothing but frustration for the researchers who testing medications.

For some reason people had this frustrating propensity to improve simply because they believed they would. It was so common and predictable that researcher who were trying to test medication had to find a way to rule out the improvement that happened because of belief. They coined this response the 'placebo effect' and at the time, they considered it just a confounding factor and kind of annoying 'fake.' response that tended to get in the way of 'real' science.

For decades, *'the placebo effect' was seen as a mere irritation that statisticians had to find a way to rule out so that they could see the 'real' efforts of the medication they were testing.* To them, the only 'real science' was the influence of chemicals that were artificially introduced into the body.

Then, one day, some researcher likely said, "This placebo thing itself if very interesting. I wonder what is going on in the brain that causes this to happen." The man or woman who first decided to look at 'the placebo effect' with the eyes of a scientist was a true genius.

'Real' science looks at a phenomenon and asks why, Real science doesn't impose our intentions of what will work on something. It starts with what is. The 'science of mindset' begins with the observing that our thoughts and beliefs do dramatically affect something measurable. All patients have a measurable tendency to improve when they believe.

But it's not just positive affects you get from belief. Scientist soon noticed the 'nocebo effects' of medication as well. The 'nocebo effect' refers to our human propensity to feel side effects or negatives effects of a treatment we expect to feel as well. When we expect things to be bad, they often are, or at least we experience them that way. The first scientifically measurable effects of mindset were noticed and compensated for in all further study.

Mindset made such a difference, that *science couldn't go on until they developed statistical ways to compensate for the fact that mindset ALWAYS and every time AFFECTED OUR BODIES.*

For years, we were so busy imposing science on our bodies

That we forgot to observe the things that were

so we could study and try to understand them.

Our thoughts, minds and beliefs have ALWAYS dramatically affected our bodies physically. The real genius in science was the person or people who said, "Something is physically going on here." Of course, what those people eventually discovered was that our belief system activates the natural OPIATE PATHWAY IN OUR BRAINS. Now, we know that our patients were not simply making this stuff up.

They actually have a chemical reason for feeling the relief they expected to feel. We now know that our brains produce natural opiates in response to our belief. What those patients were feeling were the powerful pain-relieving chemicals produced in their own brain in response to their belief. Likely, similar chemicals are responsible for the negatives we expect to feel as well.

Initial researchers began to speculate that opiates were the cause of the placebo effect (or at least one of them) of them. The way they decided to test it was completely ingenious.

NALOXONE BLOCKS THE PLACEBO EFFECT

In 1983, a group of researchers came up with a near fool-proof way to test their hypothesis. Naloxone is a drug that blocks many of the key opioid receptors in the central nervous system. If opiates were involved in the placebo effect, then Naloxone may disrupt or eliminate the placebo effects they saw in patients.

That thinking was genius. After testing their theory, these researchers found that by giving a patient Naloxone, they could prevent a large portion of the placebo effect they usually observed in their studies.[1]

After this study, we could say with much greater certainty that at least this part of the placebo effect works because our belief systems activate the natural opiate system in our brains which is responsible for pain relief. Finally, the placebo effect was no longer 'fake science' but a real and solid phenomenon that we simply had not yet understood.

Opiates were not the only brain chemical involved. It appears that our thoughts and beliefs can cause our brains to produce any chemical it naturally produces.

We can even become addicted to our own brain chemicals as we see happen in gambling and other behavioral addictions.

As soon as our brains begin to expect a certain result, be it negative or positive, the systems in our brain begin to physiologically respond.

Just as Pavlov's dogs began to salivate at the sound of a bell, some people produce excessive dopamine when they win at gambling or do other addictive behavior. The emotional and physical crash they experience when they lose is likely chemical and electrical as well. While we have yet to understand many of the chemical reactions that happen in the bodies of those with additive behaviors, the punch to the gut they feel when they lose seems to indicate extreme levels of cortisol and the adrenaline we experience when our personal safety is at stake.

---

[1] Partial antagonism of placebo analgesia by naloxone
Pain. 16(2):129–143, JUNE 1983) https://insights.ovid.com/article/00006396-198306000-00003 accessed May 5, 2020

Yes, behavior addictions are real, but behavior addictions are really chemical addictions in disguise. The body of a gambler becomes physiologically addicted to the chemical their brains create when they win. Their addictions also develop tolerance and perform like any other chemical addiction in the body. The only difference is their brains produce the chemical themselves.

It is not card playing that is addicting; it is the dopamine they have been conditioned to produce when they win that is addictive. Behavior addiction or aversion (such as fitness) is caused when our bodies are conditioned to produce a chemical response to a stimulus. We think 'fitness' and chemically, we feel 'anxiety.' When Shae thinks about fitness, she produces dopamine.

> One day I was talking to Shaelee, who was feeling a little on edge because she had not had time for her 'self-care routine' for a couple of days (meaning fitness). When she feels stressed, she has a conditioned a response of fitness, and she doesn't miss it unless she absolutely must.

Mindset works essentially like placebo and conditioning. We receive the chemical response we expect from our brains. We may not know the precise chemical recipes our brains use to respond in our heads, but we do know that they are based in expectation and the conditioned responses we have to a wide variety of situations and triggers.

> Mindset changes everything for one reason: it changes the entire chemical experience you have in your brain and our body.

During what I now think of as my recovery, I experienced a huge burst of anxiety whenever I thought about going to the gym that night. I had such a negative conditioned response to fitness in my head that I felt like I'd been hit in the gut when I thought about it. I can tell you from experience that it felt extremely chemical. I feel like it started with my junior high P.E. class. That's when I started to associate fitness with extreme pain and embarrassment. So, at first, I really had to fight myself to do it.

Once I really committed and decided to push through it, no matter how I felt about it, I finally began to get over some of that anxiety. Finally, I rewired my connection with fitness by 1) getting better at it and 2) pointing out every positive about how it made me feel when I did it.

By deciding to do it anyway, despite my anxiety, and not letting myself think about it. I simply made it as routine as I could, and I was able to motivate myself to do it long enough to experience things I liked.

For years, I didn't think that adrenaline rush really existed, at least not for me. It was likely masked by my powerful nocebo effect (the negatives I expected to experience and did) when I worked out.

I had to push through that chemical fear and anxiety response to fitness and force myself to notice everything enjoyable about the way I felt when I exercised to reprogram my brain. Conditioned response can be replaced with new conditioned responses, and I had to re-program my brain to associate positive sensations to fitness instead of negative.

If it takes an act of heroism to get yourself to work out, you may have some negative connections with it like I did.

Now, I rarely have fitness anxiety like I did. Occasionally, however, it will pop back up, especially if I stop doing it for a while or entertain the wrong kind of thoughts.

The reason mindset is so powerful is because chemically we get what we expect to receive. These placebo, nocebo, and (my newly coined term) 'eucebo effects,' feeling the euphoria or joy we expect to experience, are not imagined. They are not 'fake science.' Our brains and bodies are powerful chemical factories that produce the chemical experiences we expect to receive.

Mindset works because emotion is primarily chemical, and we get the chemical we expect to feel in response to many things in our lives. Many of us view food, fitness, ourselves, and our abilities through filters that affect the experiences. This in turn directly impacts the ability we have to accomplish our physical goals.

CONDITIONING THE PLACEBO EFFECT

As previously mentioned, many of our chemical emotional responses have been conditioned, which leads us to something else that is fascinating about a placebo. Not only does the placebo effect happen naturally, but we can intentionally condition our brains and bodies to have specific placebo reactions.

This breakthrough in our understanding of placebo work was first documented in the responses of patients that had Parkinson's disease.

> According to the Parkinson Foundation, "Parkinson's disease (PD) is a neurodegenerative disorder that affects predominately the dopamine-producing ("dopaminergic") neurons in a specific area of the brain called substantia nigra." It is associated with tremors that are impossible for a patient to control.

Parkinson's disease, therefore, is caused by a deficiency in the production of dopamine. It causes uncontrollable tremors and rigidity in the bodies of the patients who have it, and at least for now, it is an irreversible disease that is very destructive to those who have it.

To treat this condition, patients with Parkinson's are often given Levodopa (L-dopa,) a substance that converts to dopamine in the body. This medication dramatically reduces rigidity and makes tremors from the disease temporarily subside. The problem is that L-dopa, like all drugs to which we develop tolerance, becomes less effective for Parkinson's patients over time.

Dr. Luana Colloca, a leading expert in the neurobiological mechanisms that cause placebo and nocebo effects in our brains, discovered something amazing about placebo when she attempted to wean patients off it with sugar pills. She found that once a patient's brain had sufficiently associated that pill with dopamine she could 'train' the brains of some of these patients to respond in the same way to a placebo. After they had sufficiently been conditioned, their tremors would significantly reduce, and they would feel relief even when their L-dopa had been replaced with a placebo.

Just as Pavlov's dogs produced saliva at the sound of a bell, their brains and bodies had apparently learned to produce dopamine when taking that pill. Colloca learned that you can condition a response to a placebo.[2] This makes we wonder how many responses have we conditioned in ourselves because we expect to experience something in a particular way?

Apparently, a portion of the relief these patients felt was from L-dopa, but their bodies had also been 'trained' to produce dopamine to a stimulus, just as the gamblers' brains had done.

No one is considering treating Parkinson's disease with placebo alone. However, if placebo could be used for periods of time during treatment, we could potentially increase the amount to time that L-dopa is effective for treating these patients.

Colloca went on to extend this experiment to patients who required opioids for pain relief. She found that their bodies also 'learned' to produce opioids when given a placebo. Colloca speculated that after conditioning, placebo could be used to reduce opioid use in our country.

Interesting, but how does it apply to us? Many of us have conditioned nocebo responses to diet and fitness. We expect hunger and fitness to be painful or uncomfortable, and so it is.

An incredible power of mindset that can change the game for those of us who are trying to change our bodies is that when we understand it, we can begin to reprogram some of our negative mental connections.

We don't all feel the same about food and fitness. The way we feel about it is largely based on the way we expect ourselves to feel about it. In response to fitness, *some people experience severe anxiety, while others experience a dopamine high that can be exhilarating and even addicting.*

We get what we expect to feel. In life, we generally suffer over the things we expect to suffer over, struggle over the things we expect to struggle with, and feel joy and euphoria when we expect to feel it. Much of what we feel is caused by expectation! The feelings and experiences we have in our lives are often chemical placebo reactions based on what we expect to feel.

---

[2] Colloca, L. (2017, October (4th Quarter/Autumn) 6). Nocebo effects can make you feel pain. Science (New York, N.Y.), 358 (6359), 44. doi:10.1126/science.aap8488

By changing the associations you have with food and fitness in your mind, can make it significantly easier and more enjoyable to do the things it takes to live healthy. A healthy lifestyle is experienced differently by different people because of the mental connections they have made with it. Change the connections you have and at the very least, you can decide to quit suffering over these things unnecessary. We seldom recognize the extent to which we cause our own suffering in our heads.

What can you do? Begin to recognize what you expect to feel and change those connections. Recognize the chemical power of the placebo, nocebo, and eucebo effects with a wide variety of things in your life and decide to quit suffering unnecessarily.

Open your mind to the possibility of changing the experience you have with food and fitness. Start seeing yourself and the healthy lifestyle you would like to have in a whole different way that you can enjoy! Make it a quality-of-life choice. You will stop suffering and start to enjoy it when you let yourself love instead of hating it!

For years, I didn't believe in the adrenaline rush others said they experienced after fitness. It didn't happen for me largely because I didn't expect it to. I was too busy feeling all those negative things I expected. (That is when I couldn't even get myself to do it at all.)

Adrenaline is another chemical reaction our bodies have that is based on our interpretation. We may laugh at the scary startle of being followed by ominous footsteps if it is Halloween night or we know our friend is trying to startle us. While we would be terrified by those same steps if we knew we in a dark alley, or dangerous place. The chemical experience we receive in our bodies is significantly affected by our brain's interpretation. The same experience that chemically floods our bodies with fear results in just a fun and scary elevated heart rate, or even laughter if we know we are in a different setting.

Equally, our interpretations and beliefs color our world with a wide variety of emotions and chemical experiences. Our bodies act in accordance with our brain's interpretation. Brains interpret and bodies react. Chemically, we t get a rush of adrenaline, a shot of dopamine, and injection of cortisol or a flood serotonin.

A complicated 'recipe' of natural, brain and body chemicals are responsible for everything from the gut punch of fear and anxiety, to stress to the overwhelming experience of being protective or taking care of a baby that you know depends completely on you.

Mindset is so amazingly powerful because of the science behind it, even when that science is something we do not yet completely understand.

We can benefit from our belief in mindset even without understanding exactly how and why it works. Knowing our beliefs and interpretation dramatically affect our bodies chemically can give us even more motivation to keep our heads and beliefs in the place they should be.

THE REAL EFFECTS OF PLACEBO

It turns out that placebo effects were not fake at all. They were simply the powerful physical ways that belief chemically and electrically affects our bodies.

Those of us who are trying to rewire the negative connections we have with our bodies need the power of our brains to create better emotional and physical connections to fitness and a healthy lifestyle. We need to change our negative beliefs because they are chemically and emotionally affecting our bodies. We need to get the chemical and energy effects of belief on our sides. Our beliefs powerfully affect our willpower, chemicals, and ability. There are many things we can learn about ourselves from the scientific things we have learned about placebos.

1) We don't need to completely understand how mindset works to believe that it does.

2) Not even scientists fully understand how the mechanisms of placebo and nocebo work in our brains. They don't know why our thoughts matter chemically, only that they do. We are just beginning to identify the complex recipe of neurotransmitters, hormones, and catecholamines in our brains and bodies that are affected by our beliefs and perceptions. (Likely, dopamine, GABA, adrenalin, norepinephrine, cortisol, serotonin, and our the naturally produced opioids in our bodies, as well as any

other chemical our brains and bodies can naturally produce will respond to our interpretation of a situation.) In years to come, scientists will unravel how it works, but for now, we just need to know that it does.

3) Interpretation matters. If you decide you like work, you enjoy it. The way you see it and your ability to do it, matters. The same is true of the components of health. A different interpretation or mindset chemically produces a different result. For example, you respond differently to the noise you hear in a dark alley or after watching a scary show than you do after watching a love story. your interpretation of the situation matters. If you love it, you experience it differently.

4) You can retrain any negative conditioned responses you have. You are not stuck with the negative emotional reactions you may have to food or fitness. You can retrain these responses by the way you let yourself think about the experience and your ability to do it. You can reprogram the mental connections that get in your way and train yourself to have a more positive response.

DEGREES OF BELIEF

One thing we have learned is that the stronger our belief, the more powerful the relief we get from placebo. One study shows that the placebo effects you experience gets stronger with the strength of your belief.

Research has shown that the more invasive the procedure, the more placebo benefit the patient receives from it. In other words, the more you believe, the stronger the placebo effect. Researchers initially used a fake surgery to distinguish how much a patient benefited from the intervention and how much was from the placebo effect. What they found was that patient's belief in surgery is far stronger than their belief in medication. In fact, fake surgery gives patients a 75% improvement over fake medication.

Sadly, sometimes this proves that the benefits we thought came from a surgical procedure actually came from the placebo effects.

In 2002, researchers wanted to find out the effectiveness of arthroscopy on the knees of their patients with osteoarthritis.[3] To do that, they knew they had to control for the relief patients felt from the placebo effect.

In one double-blind study, participants were assigned to receive one of two different surgical interventions or a fake surgery that was designed to feel relatively the same. All patients were then evaluated using both subjective and objective measures of improvement. According to all signs, this procedure did improve the pain and function of the knee. Sadly, so did the placebo. A large portion of the patients who had surgery improved in both pain and function, but the trial failed to show with any confidence that the actual procedure outperformed the results of the fake one.

It's hard to argue with belief when you see a surgery scar on your knee, and apparently that belief that you will improve means that you will. Work on your beliefs because the stronger the belief, the more powerful the relief.

We've examined some of the chemical reactions that happen in our brains based on our thoughts and beliefs, but our brain's structure and neurology change based on our mindset as well.

MINDSET AND THE NEUROPLASTICITY OF OUR BRAINS

In her well-known book, *The Growth Mindset,* Carol Dweck explains that our brains are much more malleable and responsive to our thoughts and actions than we think they are.

We used to believe that who we were by the time we were five years old was who we would be for the rest of our lives. Now we know that our brains never stop restructuring themselves. Our brains are constantly changing and reforming themselves throughout our life based on the content we put in them.

This means we are not stuck with the brain or abilities we started with. Because of the life-long neuroplasticity of our brains, we have an

---

[3] Moseley JB, O'Malley K, Petersen NJ, Menke TJ, Brody BA, Kuykendall DH, Hollingsworth JC, Ashton CM, Wray NP. A controlled trial of arthroscopic surgery for osteoarthritis of the knee. N Engl J Med. 2002;347(2):81–8.

unlimited opportunity to change our skills, abilities, likes, dislikes, and emotions throughout our entire life span. Since our brains are constantly changing and adapting based on what we think and do, we never run out of opportunities to changes them.

NEUROLOGICAL RESEARCH CHANGES POSSIBILITY

The keynote speaker at the 25th Annual Meeting of the American Academy of Pain Medicine in Honolulu Hawaii in 2009 called this knowledge about the neuroplasticity of our brains "the most important medical advance in 400 years."[4] The knowledge that we can reshape our brains gives us control over parts of ourselves we never knew we had. By manipulating our thoughts and actions, we can rewire and retrain our brains.

According to Dr. Doidge, M.D., author of *The Brain That Changes Itself: Stories of Personal Triumph from the Frontiers of Brain Science* and a speaker at this conference, "The amount of synaptic changeover in the brain is much greater than we ever dreamed. The brain is far more malleable than we thought."

Michael Moskowitz, M.D., from the University of California Davis School of Medicine in Sacramento, was equally excited about the cutting-edge research about neuroplasticity and its application in practice. "This has implications not only for patients in chronic pain but for all humans on the planet." Our ability to manipulate and change the chemistry and structure of the brains gives us unlimited opportunities to build ability, increase willpower, and change the connection we have made with the processes that shape us. These doctors treat patients who have developed chronic pain responses that have become hard-wired into their brains. They are excited for the possibility of teaching their patients

---

[4] *AAPM 2009: Specialists Study Brain Plasticity and Its Transformative Potential, (2009) Gandy.* https://www.medscape.com/viewarticle/588275#vp_1 *accessed May 5, 2020.*

to rewire their brains much the way we are learning to rebuild the relationships we have with food and fitness.

With the lifetime of neuroplasticity that we now know exists, we can change everything we think and feel about ourselves, as well as the relationship we have with food and fitness. Since we now better understand placebo and neuroplasticity, what was once a motivational battle of epic proportion can become something you enjoy and look forward to doing. Instead of looking at your past to find out who you are, you can use mindset to rewire what made you that way.

Not only can we build muscles and change our bodies, but we now also know that through use and meditation, we can build the grey matter than is responsible for that willpower. We have heard that willpower is like a muscle that grows with use. Now we know why.

We can program new experiences into our brain muscle by repeating them until they become more normal and comfortable. We also know that if we program them with the right emotions, we develop powerful connections that affect the relationships we have with these things in the future.

Since our brains are malleable, we can use new thoughts and experiences to rewire our brains with rewarding and validating relationships to fitness and food. In turn, this will radically change the motivation we have to reach our goals.

With the right mindset,

many healthy habits can become

self-motivating on their own.

There is still so much to know about our brains and bodies that what we know now is likely only the crystals on top of the tip of the iceberg. Simply, there is a heck of a lot we still don't know.

Scientifically, we know our thoughts, beliefs and mental states affects our bodies physically. We don't yet completely understand how or why or how to best use this connection in practices, but there is no longer any medical doubt about the body and mindset connection.

We don't know everything there is to know about how our brains and bodes work together. We don't yet know why or how our thoughts have such powerful chemical and electrical effects on us physically. We don't yet understand completely the way our minds and bodies are tied together to affect each other, but we do know enough to understand the POWER OUR MINDSET has on our physical life and our body journey!

SEEK A HIGHER POWER

Seeking help from your higher power may seem to be the opposite of scientific knowledge for some, but scientifically, we have a lot to learn about the power of prayer.

Some people may believe that sincerely asking a higher power for the help is the opposite of science, I don't see it that way and neither did Einstein. Seeking help from a higher power gives many people the power they need to do it.

Einstein himself said:

> "I do not think that it is necessarily the case that science and religion are natural opposites. In fact, I think that there is a very close connection between the two. Further, I think that science without religion is lame and, conversely, that religion without science is blind."

Einstein believed religion is not empirical and that it could only be scientifically evaluated by its effect on people's lives. If I evaluate it that way, I have to say that prayer has always been there for me. When I am at the end of what I can do, or I am about to step off into something I can't see, and I sincerely asking for help, I have received a strength I didn't have on my own. When I sincerely ask for help on my knees, I feel a something powerful that helps take part of what I lack.

 I'm not telling you to become a believer. I'm just saying if you are hurting or feeling powerless, or overwhelmed, be it with your body or something else, don't rule out asking for help as an option. If you don't feel like you can, get a handle on something on your own don't rule out any options of what works. It is empirically proven that faith-based recovery systems that encourage people to turn that problem over to a higher power work, and that is enough science in it for me. You must find your own way, but that said, you may find the answer you need in prayer.

SOCIAL LEARNING

Of course, the social and psychological aspects of science are fascinating too especial the aspects of behavioral and social learning. While we are talking about the scientific aspect of mindset, let's talk just a little about the social science aspect of it too. Specifically, let's talk about the ways our mindsets are acquired through social learning in our families and communities.

POCKETS OF SOCIETY

It was years later in my life that I noticed that our physical values are often shared locally, not just in families, but in communities as well.

Pockets of society have healthy physical values, while others do not. We learn our Body Mindsets from watching and incorporating the feelings and values those around us have about how to eat and be active in their lives. The Body Mindsets we have are often learned and shared socially.

All our mindsets are deeply affected by social learning. I know mine . As we grow, we learn vicariously how to feel and be by watching the reactions and mindset of those around us. Many of our views are not our own. Rather, we picked them up from those around us.

Of course, the first connection we have with food and fitness come to us by observing the way our parents, and the people around us feel about and interact with food and fitness themselves. If they struggle or feel powerless with it, we often do as well. If they seem to enjoy it, we will likely enjoy it as well. We learn many of the values and beliefs that drive the way we see ourselves as physical human beings from our families and the views of those who were close to us as children.

My family struggled with both generational obesity and generational poverty and I can tell you now, there is so much more beauty, strength, and pain that than people know. We look at people we don't understand in such a flat way sometimes, but regardless, from my upbringing I picked up many of the mindsets I saw in those around me.

NOTE: I believe that mindsets that are passed down from generation to generation are responsible for much of the poverty and obesity we see in our country. I ALSO BELIEVE that we will not solve the obesity or poverty problems in our world until we begin to understand and do something to change the mindsets of the people who struggle with these them.

So, as I watched as my mom and grandma constantly struggle with and be stressed and powerless about the state of their bodies, I developed many of those same views myself. Both my mom and grandma were always on a diet, but never able to have much will power or ever make much progress with that. I wish the scope of the book allowed me to tell you all the beautiful and powerful sides of my life growing up, maybe some other time, but in weight and money, I inherited the belief that we were poor, and we were fat and there wasn't much we had the power to do about that.

I watched my family suffer and struggle financially and no one in my family had ever been college until I decided to break out of that and do it. Many of my close and extended family had big ideas about what they were going to do, but no one seemed to do anything powerfully enough to change that. We had dreams and goals. We wanted to change our circumstance, but our mindsets and beliefs didn't give us access to it.

Yes, I learned how to cook, and how to eat from my family. I grew up on my family's fat and carb filled comfort foods, but I also picked up on some unwritten family beliefs and powers (or rather lack of them) that taught me to feel distress, anxiety, and powerless over my physical body. I learned that I had a lack of control, which is only true if you believe it, and I learned to have anxiety about fitness as well.

It is always amazing to me how quickly we can pick up on emotional reactions those around us have in our lives or how quickly we incorporate those same reactions into our own lives just by watching.

Social learning helps us by letting us learn vicariously from those around us without having to experience their pain ourselves. Social learning also hurst us by letting us vicariously learn negative perceptions and beliefs from those around us as well. The sad part is that with both views, we are rarely ever aware that we have them. Many of the powerless views we have about ourselves physically, we could learn vicariously by watching the things those around us felt and did.

Fear and powerlessness are often socially learned. If we see someone else exhibiting fear, we also instinctively become fearful of many of those things ourselves. Social learning is a programmed into us so that we can learn from the experiences of others. It is up to us to determine if the messages we get are really the ones we should have.

As a child, my family and community shared mindsets and values that kept us fat. I just didn't see that.

COMMUNITY VALUES

I was far into my adulthood before I realized there were pockets of society that had different physical values than mine did. Before that, I had no idea that communities even had values, but they do. I had no idea that there were pockets of society that had different ways of looking at things than the one I grew up in.

Community values are visibly all around us. We just can't see them, or rather we do see them. We just think that is the way things are.

For instance, we go into the grocery store and see a magazine with the headline, "Lose 30lbs in 20 days." We pick it up and notice that right after that article about how to get our weight down in the quickest and most drastic way we can, that message this is always on the cover is followed by all those fat-filled and delicious-looking recipes in the back.

The invisible message is that losing weight is something we want to get over as soon as possible, so we can get back to living the good life in the back. The underlying message, of course, is that dieting is a necessary evil. It needs to be quick and drastic so we can get it done and get back to real life.

POCKETS OF SOCIETY

It's not just families that have unhealthy physical values. Communities have them, too! I still remember the day it dawned on me that pockets of our society really love and enjoy healthy food and a healthy life.

THE RAW FOOD RESTAURANT

Once my daughter took me to a raw food restaurant on the East side of Salt Lake City. It was an interesting neighborhood that maintained its upper scale feel to it even though most of the houses were more than 100 years old.

This is the first time I noticed or coined the phrase, 'pockets of society' in my head. I think it was the first time I ever noticed that communities could have values and mindsets of their own.

This interesting little neighborhood, didn't have the pretentious wealth or putting on airs of those trying to keep up with the Jones.' It didn't have the high stress of people trying to live above their means powerlessness of those who feel stuck where they don't want to be. Rather, it was just a comfortable little neighborhood of people who obviously valued simplicity, art (as seen by all the cute little artisan shops around town) a place that was slow enough to see and connect with each other and admire things, healthy eating, and choosing to live an active life.

As we were sitting in this restaurant, overlooking Salt Lake, I noticed some differences I wasn't used to. In front of it was a bike rack. It appeared that many of the people eating and obviously enjoying each other's company had biked over to eat there that day. Not only that, but there was a bike shop on one side, a child's dance, and karate studio on the other, a place to buy simple and tasteful clothes that could move and a health food store in place of the grocery store you would normally find in the middle. Obviously missing, at least to me were the fast-food restaurants, a place to buy fries of fried chicken, and a movie theater where you could go for passive entertainment.

In their places were people who seemed be enjoying this lifestyle of activity and healthy eating as a quality-of-life choice. Personally, I was just transitioning to a healthy lifestyle of my own. Maybe that is why I noticed it to the extent that I did. s

What I had never considered much was the not everyone ate 'rabbit food' to punish themselves for getting too fat. Most of the people who were eating like this and being active like that seemed to be loving it.

Three things (beyond how much I loved the food), really hit me that day.

1. **The first being that communities have values**. It is not just families that teach us how to be or see the world. Our communities do too! Something about that day helped to formulate my ideas about Body Mindset in my head.
2. **Second, it was clear to be that not everyone felt the way I had seen people feel about food and fitness**. The people out there running or riding their bikes were not punishing themselves or drastically trying to lose weight. Instead, they seemed to enjoy it.
3. **Finally, there is a way of thinking and seeing things that changes the way you experience a healthy lifestyle**. I think that day it really dawned on me that I had options for how to feel about living this way. Instead of stress, or rushed or powerless, to me, this lifestyle looked like a good way to be.

WE HAVE OPTIONS FOR HOW TO FEEL

Before we can ever begin to realize the power of mindset, we must begin to realize that we have options for how to think, feel about and see the things around us. Mindset is about options. It is also about recognizing the consequences of how we think, see, and feel about something on our behavior, and our effectiveness in our lives.

Families have Body Mindset or invisible ways they feel about and approach health or lack of it in the way that they live. Communities also have heath values that send powerful messages to the people that live in them However, it is up to us to realize that the way we see, and feel doesn't have to come from our social cues.

We must get intentional about seeing and feeling in ways that will best support our body health, goals, and success.

The power of mindset comes from the understanding that in everything in our lives, we have the choice of what to think and how to see the things around us. We can choose to accept or reject the views of others in favor of the views, beliefs and emotions that are best for us, our goals and the quality of life and body that we want we have decided to have.

MODEL HEALTHY VALUES FOR THOSE YOU LOVE

Knowing the power of social learning can give you one other good reason to live in a better place with food and fitness. You don't just receive social cues about a Body Mindset, you send them as well.

One of the best reasons to live and enjoy that healthy lifestyle and positive connections with healthy food in your life is that others around you will learn from your physical values as well. If you want your kids to grow up valuing and living in ways that will keep them healthy, model that healthy lifestyle and your own good feelings about it for them.

Sure, you socially learned your Body Mindset from others around you. Depending on your circumstance, that could have gone well or badly. However, you have values to pass forward as well.

The way you physical live can tell your kids, 'We love to be active.' 'Our best times together are spent at a park or on a park or outside actively exploring.' 'We eat healthy food and it's good!' 'My parents work out every day. This looks like the thing people do.'

When it comes to Body Mindsets, you inherited a way to physically live from the past, and you have one to pass it forward as well. You communicate that living healthy is just what we do, and loving is it is how we feel about it vicariously when those around you see you actively living and enjoying that healthy life yourself!

> Develop positive ways to see yourself, healthy food, and fitness. One reason to create a healthy body mindset and to not just do it, but to learning to love it, want to do it, and think about it positively is for you. The other is so you can pass that healthy Body Mindset forward to others in the future. By your emotion and your action in that life, others are also learning how to feel.

Shaelee and her husband Bray are the perfect example of family values that include a healthy lifestyle. The way they are raising their kids is a completely different experience than the childhood experiences I had.

Shaelee, Bray, and their kids are always out doing something active. They go on hikes, ride bikes, swim, climb, run, play, and jump together and their parents are out there doing it and loving it too! Family fun involves activity. Family meals are built around vegetables, protein, fruit, and other healthy food. Their kids don't even see another way to eat or live. When I go over, I will likely find that Shaelee is roller blading with the kids at the park or her and her two-year-old doing their squats in the living room. They have fun with it! Growing up with the healthy values is not something I had. Shaelee models her love of a healthy lifestyle for them by enjoying it with them. Her kids will not have to overcome the feelings of fear and anxiety I had about activity this life that I did.

Shaelee's kids only rarely eat sugar. They don't have it in the house, and they don't miss it because Shaelee can make a healthier version of almost everything. Life is good when the values you learn at home are the ones that will keep you living healthy and being happy about it for the rest of your life.

Make your family memories and happy times healthy ones as well. Family fun should be active fun that the parents are involved in as well. If kids go out to play while parents crash on the couch, kids learn different physical values than if everyone gets out there, connects with each other and has fun. Without a socially modeled active and connected way to have fun, kids spend their time on TV or video games.

Now, I am so grateful that in a family that suffered from generational poverty and obesity for generations, we broke those socially taught values and kids and their kids have developed a better relationship with healthy food and fitness from the start.

NEVER LET YOUR HEAD PUT A
LIMIT ON A THINGS YOUR
BODY CAN DO

The Body Mindset

TO SUM IT UP:

Scientifically, there is much we still need to learn about the chemical and electrical ways our thoughts affect our bodies physically and the state of our bodies affect our minds. However, there is no longer any scientific doubt that they do. The state of our minds dramatically impacts things as diverse as our blood pressure and other vital signs, to the chemical structure of our brains and our bodies.

We also have empirical evidence that our beliefs affect us too. Some of the best evidence for the effects of our belief is the placebo effect. We have a lot to learn, but we now believe that the placebo effect happens because our bodies product the chemicals we expect to receive. If we expect pain reduction, our bodies flood our neurotransmitters with the biochemical equivalent of morphine. If we expect to enjoy something, we get a dose of the brain chemical serotonin.

The things we think, believe, and feel have a very real impact on our bodies that we are likely decades or even centuries away from fully understanding or utilizing in medicine and healthy intervention.

Mindset is powerful because it creates dramatic changes

MORE ABOUT MY WEIGHT LOSS STORY

I was perhaps the last girl you would ever expect to write a book like this. I have never been the poster child for fitness. I struggled with weight and inactivity my whole teenage and adult life. Most of my life I thought there must be something wrong with me because no matter how hard I tried, I couldn't seem to get myself, my weight, or my body under control. but I have always been a believer in mindset.

Finally, after a lifetime of frustration and hundreds of diets and fitness plans, I was lucky enough to find the solution I needed for me. I found the power of mindset. I learned it wasn't my body, it was my mind that was keeping me from getting there Luckily, I learned that the only real way to change my body is to change into the mental place it takes to make it happen.

There never was anything wrong with me. The only reason I couldn't get myself to do it was my state of mind. The reason I didn't have willpower and I couldn't consistently stick with a diet or exercise plan was that I didn't really believe it would work and I never fully committed to making it happen. Momma used to tell me that I could do anything I set my mind to, but she never told me I had to 'set my mind' to the goal of changing my body as well. Of course, I doubt that my mom ever knew that herself.

I didn't even realize I had a mindset problem. I thought I needed to find the right diet or to get rid of my stress. I didn't know that I had beliefs that were making me unable to do this.

I didn't know that people who were not obese and inactive had a different way of seeing themselves and the process. I certainly didn't know that way of thinking was an option for me.

In fact, I didn't understand fit and healthy people at all. The way they thought was a complete mystery to me. Luckily, an association with a few dear friends who were very different from me and my family, helped me realize there was a different mental place I could be in. Until then, I didn't know there was an option to see things differently from what I had felt and had seen as a child. I didn't even know I had a Body Mindset, much less that the thoughts and views I held were making it harder for me.

I certainly couldn't fathom why some people seemed to enjoy that lifestyle. I thought they must have been born that way. I naturally didn't love fitness or have good willpower from birth, or so I thought. I thought it wasn't me, but it was the beliefs I had about me and the process that were making it true.

Now, I watch my daughter Shaelee's kids who were raised in a fit and active household, and I see how much of this mindset we learn from our upbringing. I understand where I was even more. I was raised by an overweight and often overwhelmed single mother who felt out of control physically. We ate carb loaded comfort foods and had inactive fun. I saw my mom and grandmother stressed and unhappy about their bodies and ineffectively try to change them.

Now, it makes complete sense to me. I wasn't born that way. I learned the mindset I had in the largely overweight and poor society I grew up in. Please don't get me wrong, I LOVED my childhood. My childhood made me who I am in so many ways. I just had to learn that not all I learned was positive.

I became curious about the way of thinking and living that I saw in some of my fit friends. Maybe I could try to see it from their point of view, then understand and emulate their mindset and behavior. Surely, there was some piece in my mind I was missing that would give me the power I needed to take control mentally and physically.

Well guess what? That was exactly true. All the struggling I did in one mindset was not there in a different one. All the anxiety and powerlessness I felt came from the glasses I was seeing things through. A fit and competent mindset changes your motivation, ability, and happiness levels in general, and every different mindset gives you a different experience and set of outcomes.

I had to mentally agree to see fitness with different eyes and I had to make a new commitment to it. When I did, I quit fighting the process like I had my entire life.

As part of the Physical Success Plan I made for myself, I had to create and agree to a new set of mental and physical rules and commit to follow those rules even in the worst of times. I was becoming a new person physically, and that required stretching out of my comfort level to explore a new way of being.

When I finally got my head in the right place and committed to it, I quit fighting myself and the process. I was finally motivated to change my eating and activity level, and I lost nearly a hundred pounds. That was over ten years ago. I wish I could go back and tell my younger self that I could have had a different mentality than the one I knew.

If you are in the place I was in, I hope I can save you years or decades of time. I want to show you that there is a different mental place you can be in this area; you have the choice of a better Body Mindset.

In the right mindset, getting your body in a better place is not as hard as you thought it was. You must get your head in the right mental place to do it and keep it there. Body fitness and a healthy weight are just the product of good consistent body routine that you won't excuse yourself out of. Once you get going in the right direction, you must mentally commit to stay there. See it and yourself in the right way and your body goals and far easier than your thought. I wish I knew then what I now know about mindset. I wouldn't have struggled with it as much as I did.

MY CHALLENGES

I went through this big physical change not in the absence of challenge, but during one of the hardest parts of my life. So, you see that I didn't wait for the challenges in my life to be gone, let me tell you some of the things I was going through when I did it.

The decision that changed my life came to me because of my mom's debilitating stroke. It also happened in the middle of a housing crisis and a very messy divorce in my life that left me as the sole emotional and financial supporter of six kids ages 3 to 13.

During that divorce, my husband and I lost the house that we had built ourselves. To avoid foreclosure, we had to sell our beautiful home for barely what we owed on to. We went from living in a beautiful house to literally having nowhere to go. The kids and I spent the first night in a car and I had no idea where I was going to go. Finally, my sister let me temporarily move into her place until I find somewhere to go.

I had no job, no money, no education, no financial help, and no idea how I was going to do this! I was also emotionally devastated. Physically, I let myself melt down and spiral out of control by eating badly and gaining a lot of weight, which only made it worst! When my mom had that stroke, none of that changed, except the decision to go in a different direction with my body. It was crazy stressful, yet I was determined to not let all that stress get in the way of this decision I had made to turn things around and make some new physical rules for me and my body.

I eventually found a tiny run-down, single wide trailer the kids and I could move into. It had two bedrooms for seven of us, a leaky roof, and numerous other problems, but it was something we could get into temporarily (which ended lasting for about 4 years.)

It was in that situation that I heard about my mom's stroke and I made the decision that I would physically not going that way again. It was also in that situation that I made another hard decision in my life: I was going to go to college.

No one in my family had ever gone to college. I had no one there to help me or show me the ropes. I was doing that alone after a divorce, with no money and while raising six kids by myself when my mom had her stroke, and I made that decision. I tell you that, so you don't fall for the trap of thinking you need the right conditions in your life.

When things are hard, I usually justify eating I shouldn't do. Yet, when I made the decision that I was done going in that physical direction in my own life, I did it during one of personally and emotionally hardest times of my life. This proves that we don't' have to have the right conditions to make this work. We just have to get our heads around doing it the right way and decide that, without excuse, we are going to change the direction we are going with our bodies. .

We must quit letting our challenges justify our bad body behavior! I know the struggle is real. Really, I get it! But you don't have to let your struggle do bad things to you.

You are the master of your life, not the slave to it. You can make decision to quit justifying you own physical meltdowns and bad behavior.

It is not necessary to wait until things get easier in your life to change. Instead, we must become the master of our lives and make decisions on the direction we are going to go without all that reactive behavior and thought that we use to justify us getting stuck. Life doesn't have to get easier so you can do this. You just need to get your head in the place it takes to stay on course and make it happen.

Lack of challenge in our live is not the prerequisite we let ourselves think it is.

When you get your head in a different place, no other challenge in your life has the power to bring you down I you refuse to let it.

Get in the driver's seat and make some decision of where you are going to go, regardless of whether things line u and make that easy to do or not!

FIND YOUR POWERFUL WHY

Tony Robbins, perhaps the world' greatest performance coach, tells us that to get motivated we need to find our own powerful why. My reason became to be there for my kids and grandkids the way my mom would never have the chance to do. I did it for time and a quality of my life I didn't want to lose now or in the future.

When I got that phone call about the devastating stroke my mom had when she was just 57 years old, I mentally flipped the switch in my mind that I was done going in that direction myself, and I mentally committed to get on track physically and stay there.

Without anything else changing, I decided to not excuse that kind of behavior from myself again. I decided to get on track and stay on track, and after I made the right decision to do it, I did!

Don't wait for easier time to begin
Or you might be waiting for it forever.

Out of self-disclosure, I must also tell you that after ten years of good fitness, and weight management, I let two things combine to mess with my head and make me spin out in the wrong direction once again.

First, my mom took herself off dialysis and we took her home to die. Instead of the 7 to 10 days they told us however, we became her nearly constant care takers for 21 months. Then, in the middle of mom being on hospice, (and me still teaching full time) along came Covid-19. It was crazy hard and once again I let that mess with my head.

We lost mom on June 4th, 2020, I knew I had gotten back onto a weak and powerless slippery slope with my body and my mind. Luckily, I recognized the mental and physical spiral I was falling back into much earlier this time, and this time, I felt confident that I could set my mind on getting back on trac with my body and do it. After doing it once, this time I had no doubt that I could and I would, and I did!

I gained 30lbs in the 21 months my mom was on hospice, and a few more in the months that followed as my normal routine and mindset were interrupted by both her care and Covid-19. After 10 years of thinking weight would never be a problem for me again because I had changed, I gained 30lbs over that year and a half.

MY OWN SLIP

After ten solid years of being fit and healthy, I thought I had changed. And that part was no longer inside me. However, I regretfully admit that after my mom went on hospice, I justified letting myself fall back into my old ways of eating badly and not working out. When mom took herself off dialysis, they gave her 7 to 10 days to live, which probably wouldn't have hurt me physically too badly, however, that 7 to 10 days became a year and half and I put on 30lbs and physically and mentally spun out of control when I did.

It is a miracle this book is even out there, because after I slipped myself, I closed my computer on a nearly finished book because I no longer felt qualified to write it. After ten good years of understanding what I mentally and physically had to do, I lost the mojo I had with my own mind and my body for a bit, and I quit writing when I did.

After my mom's death on June 4, 2020, I found myself in a different mental and physical place than I had been before. Everything, including the pandemic, and a particularly hard time I was having at school, found me in a different mental and physical place.

MY BOOK SAVED ME

I was right in the middle of my own mental and physical meltdown, when I picked up an old copy of this book I had laying around and started to read.

It was as if I had written this book completely for myself, which I guess I did, but the words on these pages were exactly what I need to hear. My own book spoke to me in a way that reached me and pulled me out of that place I was in. It took my own book to pull me out of it and put me back on track!

FINALLY, I UNDERSTOOD THE POWER OF THIS BOOK and I knew why I had to finish it. I had to finish this for myself and I had to finish it for my readers.

I wrote the book for me, and for you, but with my own slip, the purpose of it became completely clear to me. WE MUST GET OUR HEADS IN THE RIGHT PLACE. We can take control of our lives physically and mentally and live our life the way we should. I strongly believe in the power of this book. It saved me by helping me get my head back into the place it had to be to take care of myself the way I should, and it can do the same for you. Finally, I KNEW that this book was far too valuable to sit in my computer and let me feel like a fraud for writing it. I got my head around finishing it so it could do the same for you.

SUFFERING IS OPTIONAL

It takes a long time in life to realize
that suffering in life is optional.

.

As with many things SUFFERING OVER OUR BODY AND WHAT IT TAKE TO CHANGE THEM IS OPTIONAL.

Sometimes we suffer over our bodies and the processes of change and caring for them far more than we should. When you finally realize that you mentally suffer and struggle over this part of the journey for more than you should, you take a major turn in the Body Mindset you need to get happy and effective at living in a healthy way.

Choice over suffering requires some mental self-restraint. Of course, not everyone who reads this book will quit suffering overeating right and working out. Some people who read this will begin to recognize that suffering over this, as it is over all things, is really a choice.

Lacking willpower, having low energy, low motivation or staying in a low mood are optional, too.

When you see the power of choosing your own perspective, a whole world of choice about what you experience opens to you. Like most other suffering we do in life. suffering over your body goal and the processes of healthy living is a choice.

Deciding to see and experience the process differently can take all the suffering out of it.

Change the way you see those goals and the processes of change. and they actually get far easier to do.

Don't let healthy food and fitness be a mental battle in your head. Refuse to battle with or suffer over that process in your head. When you refuse to suffer or experience it like that, getting your body where you want it to be gets easier to do.

CHAPTER
THREE

GLASS CEILINGS AND MAILBOXES

O ver the years, two mindset concepts have become life changing for me. These are the concepts of glass ceilings and mailboxes. In this application, glass ceilings don't refer to the limits of women in the workplace but rather the limits we put on ourselves in our heads.

Over the years, two mindset concepts have become life changing for me. These are the concepts of glass ceilings and mailboxes. In this application, glass ceilings don't refer to the limits of women in the workplace but rather the limits we put on ourselves in our heads.

Without meaning to, we often create invisible mental limits on what we think we can do. When we beliefs we are not good at something, or we believe we don't like it, we often create a mental glass ceiling over our ability in that area that keeps us from seriously trying to go any higher.

For whatever reason, our doubts about our ability in that area, our fears about what it will be, or our belief that it will be more uncomfortable than we can handle make us shy away from any serious attempt to perform beyond that limit we created over ourselves in an area of our lives.

We begin to develop some beliefs about who we are and what we can and can't do that sometimes forms a limit over us and the things we seriously attempt to do. We think we know ourselves and our limits and before we know it, we are unable to get ourselves to get out of the that box.

As soon as we say, I'm not good at this, and that's just who I am, or I'm scared of this thing and I don't dare approach it, we build a glass ceiling over our effort and even our ability that prevents us from going any further.

We think we know ourselves and within that, we think we know our limits, and guess what? We are right, because as soon as we believe we have a limit or we're not good at something, we believe it true. We create a mental barrier in our minds that makes us avoid it or makes us put in only a superficial show of effort that proves we can't do that thing. With our beliefs and fears, we create a glass ceiling over our abilities that prevents us from going as high as we can in some area of our lives.

GLASS CEILINGS ARE INVISIBLE

The problem with glass ceilings is we don't always know we have them. Most of glass ceilings are invisible to us. When we can't do something or we can't get ourselves do something, we usually have no idea why. We don't know we are mentally blocking ourselves from doing that thing or being effective with it.

One of the reason glass ceiling hurt us so badly is they are invisible. We see that belief as a real limit or area of weakness in ourselves so they make us think the problem lies in us.

We are often blind to the ways we limit ourselves. We think there is something wrong with us, or that we legitimately can't, and we have no idea we have created a mental limit on ourselves in that area of our lives.

Mental limits cause us to avoid, procrastinate, and put mediocre effort into the things that we do because we really think we can't, or it won't work out for us even if we do. When we have a glass ceiling or mental limit over our ability in some area of our lives, we either avoid that thing or we approach it with less effort than it takes to get it done.

GLASS CEILINGS AFFECT OUR BODIES

Often the reason we physically are the way we are is we have created some mental limits and beliefs about ourselves and our willpower and the things we can accomplish physically.

We just don't see ourselves as being able to stick with this thing and lose that weight and workout every day in our minds. We have blocked that area of behavior with a glass ceiling that tells us we can't in our mind.

Often the reason we are ineffective with our body goals, is we just can't see ourselves really doing those things or getting to the other side in our minds.

GLASS CEILINGS ARE CREATED BY FEAR

Glass ceilings are lack of belief, but they are also created by fear. Usually, we don't even know what we fear, and sometimes we fear failure if we try. Certainly, we fear uncertainty. We fear what we may feel, and we almost always imagine it in a way that affects what we actually experience (read the placebo effect in chapter two.)

When we fear the unknown and doubt that we can do it, it changes the way we attempt it and the determination and resilience we have when we do. Faced with our own fear and doubt, we don't make a serious attempt to fly through that window and get to the other side because we really think we can't. When we have a glass ceiling of doubt over selves in an area, we don't attack that goal with the real intent and determination it takes to be successful with that goal.

We hold back on our effort and are quick to quit because we think we can't. We fear we will fail. We are secretly scared, and with all those mental limits we have over ourselves in that area of our lies, we approach that goal so tentatively and break-ably that we are unable to get past that mental limit we think we have.

Essentially, we approach that limit so tentatively and break-ably that it is impossible for us to be effective with it. Essentially, that limit we think we have, prove themselves to be true every time!

We still set and try our goals. We attempt them with all the hope that this time we will win the lottery and our motivation and ability will suddenly fall into place and we will, but we never do because we don't really believe it and it's not really the way we see ourselves. We mentally have about as much faith in our ability to accomplish that goal as we do in winning that lottery. Often, we think winning the lottery would be a whole lot more likely.

GLASS CEILINGS AFFECT OUR RESILIENCE

When we have belief, we approach that goal with determination and a resilience that make us determined not to stop when things go wrong.

Without belief, those glass ceilings wreck our resilience. We quit easily and talk ourselves out of it when anything is not easily predictable in our body goals. Without resilience, we can't handle any struggle or physical sensation we are not used to.

We are not mentally prepared to get through hunger or cravings. We can't handle getting winded. We think we are going to die when we experience something we are not used to feeling. Our anticipation of it feeling bad colors our experience and makes us easily breakable when we feel anything at all.

Instead, we must realize that in the right mindset, the things we experiences are nothing we can't handle. We can get into the mindset to handle our workouts or changes in our eating, or we can fear and over experience them. Sometimes, we psych ourselves out with even the slightest sensation or fear of one long before we get close to reaching any actual physical limit. We get scared of experiencing or doing something not familiar. We are not mentally prepared for doing that and the mental limits and fears we have prevented us from ever reaching any real physical limits of our body or ability.

Most often, our mental limits shut us down, not our physical ones.

When we take on a body goal, we mentally commit to it 'as long as it doesn't get too hard' or 'if life doesn't throw us a curve ball.' We commit mentally to our goals as long as our mood is right, and nothing else is added on or unpredictable in our life. We commit to our body goals, but we do it in a very breakable way that comes with a backout plan for failure in case it seems too hard. We commit with a big IF STATEMENT attached. We give ourselves a backout clause, like this. "I'll eat right today UNLESS I have a really tough day at work." We don't say it or even think it, but that big if statement that is there in our commitment if we need to get out, and of course, we will have far too many times that we use it. If fact, if we allow exceptions, we will likely find more and more reasons that excuse us from it until we quit. . '

We must get mentally resilient. We must take away the option to not eat that way or not workout that day. We must make a NO EXCUSE POLICY for doing this in our head and put our body goals at the top of our list of priorities so we will be resilience and strong in our determination to get them done.

Belief changes us. The belief that we can't or that we can't handle the way it feels makes us weak and breakable. The belief that nothing can get in our way, and we will find a way to do this regardless of what else happens that day, makes us strong, determined, resilient and ultimately successful at the things we set out to do.

Of course, like if not going to go as planned. When we commit 'if it's not too hard and things go right' we break easily when things don't go the way we planned. With that attitude, nearly anything that comes up in our lives will seem to legitimate reason to excuse ourselves from doing it.

Then, we mentally say, "Look, I failed again. I knew I wasn't good at this. This is not me. I'm not good at this. I always fail at this. I don't have willpower. My life is too hard. I just can't do this, and we create a glass ceiling that intimidates us out of it again. We plan for failure. We build in an out. We take that out and let ourselves eat badly that day or not workout. We plan to fail. Then we fail, and mentally tell ourselves we were right. "See, I'm not at this, and here's some proof."

Until we believe we can, our efforts will always be far too breakable to work.

WE CAN SHATTER GLASS CEILINGS

However, the glass ceilings we have in our live are not our real limits. They really limit us because they keep us from being resilient and determined enough to do it, but they are not our real limits.

Glass ceilings are nothing more than a set of limiting beliefs that we need to challenge and get determined to break through.

Shattering our own glass ceilings means attacking our goals with the determination and intention it takes to prove them wrong.

Like a bird afraid of hitting its head on a limit it thinks is there, glass ceilings work because they make us avoid a goal or hold back and not put our full effort or resilience into our attempt to achieve it. Shattering a glass ceiling means hitting a goal with the mental determination and resilience it takes to knock it out of the park and get past limits we used to think we had in our heads.

Shattering a glass ceiling is proving one of your old limiting beliefs wrong by getting determined enough to stick with it until you do.

GLASS CEILINGS MAKE US FEEL LESS THAN ENOUGH

One of the biggest problems with glass ceilings is the crushing blow it deals to our self-esteem when we think we are not enough.

When we feel like a failure, we perform like one. When we feel less than enough is some way, we feel frustration at ourselves because we can't, or we are not very good at something in our lives. We naturally hate to fail, and we hate to feel like we are not enough. In fact, it is one of the most painful experiences of our lives. Because we all hate failure and that feeling that we are not enough, we often back away from any challenge we think will end in defeat. By avoiding something we think we might fail, we always ensure that we do. .

Glass ceilings are both painful and invisible because they take away our effort, ability, competence, and the self-esteem we need to feel good about ourselves and do the things we do.

One of the biggest problems with glass ceilings is they are often invisible to the people who have them. We can't see that we are mentally limiting ourselves with a limiting belief. We just think it's real. We think we legitimately are not good at something. We take that belief into our identities in a way that makes it real.

The glass ceilings of beliefs about limits and weaknesses we have are not real. Our beliefs about our limits are not real limits at all. In fact, there is no such things as a real limit. Like a mirage in the desert, the closer you get to what looks like your limit, the more you improve and the further out that limit seems. You can't really reach a limit, because as you do, your ability grows. Really, limits don't exist. We all have the ability for unlimited growth in every direction we choose.

Glass ceilings make us shy away from challenge in fear of a limit. Glass ceilings are the only real limit we have because they shut down the effort it takes to get better. When we believe we can't, we don't, and we don't get better when we don't try. Instead, try to reach the extent of your limits and you find you don't have one. Approach what you think is a limit with the real intent and determination to achieve a goal and you will.

Like the fence an animal believes is electrified, a glass ceiling has no real ability to stop you from getting what you want at all. Mental ceilings only limit us if we believe in them and limit and stop ourselves!

Breaking though the mental barriers that stop us from getting new places, requires only that we challenge our limits with the determination and resilience it takes to really get there.

Too often we believe we don't have the ability to stick with our body goals, lose the weight, do those workouts consistently or get through the hunger and inconvenience that we worry about.

Really, most of the time, the actual physical sensations are not that bad. By the placebo effect (or rather the nocebo effect), we experience hunger and our workout as worse than it is. We expect it to be terrible or difficult, and that is the way we experience it.

Getting through that glass ceiling is a two-part process. We need more determination in order to do it, AND we need to quit seeing it in ways that makes it harder than it is!

With our mindset, we need to change the way we experience the experience and physical sensations that make us quit when we do.

Sometimes the reason we melt down physically or are unable to stick with our body goals is fear and a negative expectation makes us freak out when we feel anything we are not used to feeling or doing.

We avoid, and anticipate discomforted and those beliefs, combined with the belief that this is not us and we can't, cause us to back away from a fence that can't even contain us. It's not a limit. It's just a mindset that scares us and tells us we can't.

Glass ceilings, therefore, are not real. They are simply a mirage created out of fear of the things that we don't know and are not yet comfortable with.

REFUSE TO BELIEVE YOU HAVE LIMITS

As human beings, our tendency is to pull away from the things we think we can't do, or we think we won't really be good at.

Glass ceilings happen because we pull away from the things we think we're not good at. By doing this, we prove to ourselves that we can't. We believe we have a limit or weakness in an area of our lives, and we pull away, and don't challenge that.

Of course, we become worse and weaker at the things we avoid. We avoid and get weaker at something, which further proves that we can't, and over time, we become compliant and learn to stay within that box that we created for ourselves in our minds. Really, the limits we think we have, are only in our heads. Maybe we are weak at first in that area, but that weakness was cause by avoiding. We can't expect to start strong. We often must start weak at something in order to get strong.

Because the mental limits in our heads are not real, they can't stop us once we get determined not to let them.

How do you break through your own glass ceilings? You quit approaching your goals so tentatively that you break down and excuse yourself out of them when things aren't perfect. You get rid of your back-out plan that you hold onto in case you need to fail. You get determined to get through this day or that workout instead of looking for a way out of around. You decide the only way out is through, and you take away the mental option you give yourself to quit or to fail.

Glass ceilings are maintained by fear. They are fear of the unknown. They are fear of our limits. They are fear of what we may feel, and they are fear of our secret belief that we can't.

Fear makes us hyper ready to quit. To shatter our glass ceilings, we need to get intentional. Get resilient and get determined to not allow a mythical belief about a limit we have in our mind tell us what we can or can't do with ourselves physically.

Start to see yourself as a person who can and who will create this amazing makeover in your mind and your body. Begin to see yourself as a person who accomplishes the things you set your mind on doing.

Quit believing you can't. instead get determined to shatter all those old, ineffective beliefs you have in your head and prove to yourself (the most important person to prove it to) that you can. Don't let yourself feel flawed or not good at something you want to do. Don't believe in limits and things you can't do. Limits are not real anyway.

Instead, believe in your own determination and resilience to accomplish the things you set your mind on doing. If you think you can't, or you think you are not good at something, then it's time to set your sights on proving to yourself that you can and that you will. If you find a glass ceiling where your beliefs in your ability to do something are low, get determined to prove to yourself that you can.

Sometimes, you must often challenge and change your own beliefs about you before you will find the power to get effective and achieve your body goals.

Don't let yourself have limits on what you can do in your mind. Instead, embrace the power of yet. It might take a little determination. You'll likely fall down a few times, or many before you get where you want to be, but there are no real limits and mental limits only stop you if you let them. So, refuse to allow any limiting beliefs about who you are, or the thing you can't do. Don't ever let the image you have of yourself be weak, ineffective, uncaring, or unhealthy. Instead, actively create and embrace a view of yourself and things that empowers you to be the person you want to be.

Get in the mindset it takes to push the limits of your beliefs and abilities. Get determined to challenge your own mental beliefs about who you are and the things you can do. Get prepared to challenge your own limiting identities and to shatter that glass ceilings of belief that are limiting you and preventing you from doing the things you can do if you get your head in the place it takes to do them!

INTENTIONALLY CREATE A NEW IMAGE

The way we see ourselves is too vastly important to be unintentional. Our self-images are far too important to be formed casually and reinforced by becoming a self-fulfilling prophecy as we behavior in a way that validates our bad belief. We must get intentional about the image we have of ourselves and our ability to do the things we want to do. We must intentionally see ourselves as the powerful and effective people we want to be.

Our self-image determines everything we do and the way that we do it. It determines our effort, our resilience and even the way we experience the things that we do. Our self-image is FAR TOO IMPORTANT to let it be formed as randomly or casually as we often do. We must get more intentional about the way we see ourselves and how determined we are to accomplish the things we set out to do.

In short, you MUST GET MORE INTENTIONAL about the way you see yourself, and your limits or lack of them in your head!

You can't be a fat kid who is not good at physical things or self-control in your head and make any real progress with your body. . You can't afford to allow a mindset that is weak, ineffective, or unhealthy.

> Become a fit and healthy person who can in your mind, and you will become one in your life as well!

The beliefs you have about yourself, along with your fears and mental limit and expectations for how you will experience these things will create a glass ceiling over your ability or open up the sky as the limit for what you can do. Your belief about your ability to do will dramatically change your life and behavior.

ACTIVELY DECIDE HOW TO SEE YOURSELF

You must actively decide how to see yourself. That means you can't see yourself through the eyes of anyone who doesn't see you as strong or powerful, including yourself.

The way you see yourself, not only determine how you feel, it also determines nearly everything about the things you do, including how effectively you do them.

You must get intentionally about seeing yourself in ways that are in line with who and what you want to be so you can.

What you see and believe about you is self-validating because if you believe it, you will behave it true. Like being aware of the white cars in the parking lot, they are suddenly all around you. Get focused on your own weakness and you will see it all around and encourage it.

Our beliefs are self-validating . We see and find 'evidence' for whatever we believe. The ones we have about ourselves are even worse because we behave in a way that actually 'creates' proof. It doesn't matter I you believe you can, or you can't, you're right because we behave our beliefs and self-concepts to be true. .

We must actively decide to view ourselves in way that are consistent with who we want to be and where we want to go.

GROWTH MINDSET

The biggest reason to challenge those limits is because they are wrong. In truth, there are no limits.

In her book, *Growth Mindset*, Carol Dweck taught us that when we see ourselves with a 'fixed mindset' we believe we have fixed inherent traits and abilities that defines us and is part of who we are. A fixed mindset is not just ineffective, but also inaccurate. Really, our brains and abilities remain plastic and changeable throughout our lives. We don't really have any fixed attributes or limits at all because we can grow and change our brains and our abilities all our lives.

The intricate and beautiful network of connections in our brains that give us our ability and make us who we are is always capable of growth. Really, there is no such thing as a static, fixed trait of any kind.

.Fixed mindsets are an inaccurate picture of who we are or the shape and ability we have. We may be out of shape now, but that is a place. It is not an identity. Growth mindsets don't come with that 'this is me' Fixed identity of who we are that gets us stuck.

DEVELOP A GROWTH MINDSET

Work on your belief that you have no limits, only an unlimited ability to grow and improve in every direction. There are no inherent weaknesses you have or things you can't do. Sure, you are in different places with different things. That doesn't matter at all when it comes to growth. Al that does, is if you shy away from that thing and the effort it takes to improve.

Growth mindsets always see the possibility of improvement. They always see effort and determination as the force it takes to get there.

The struggles we have with our bodies and our body goals so often comes from a fixed belief about who we are physically and fixed set of abilities and limits we have in our minds.

FIXED MINDSETS ABOUT AGING

As we get older, we expect to decline and to some extent that is true. However, much of the way that we age will depend on what we expect of ourselves when we do. Fixed mindsets say this is us and we won't get any better.

Even worse than that, is expecting to decline. When we expect to decline and lose ability, we quit trying in a way that makes that be true.

As we get older, we must be careful about what we expect the aging process to be because we are going to believe that true for ourselves as well. If you lower our expectations and expect to decline, we will quit trying to do anything else.

Growth Mindset must be continued throughout our life. If you are living, you should be growing. Life is growth. There is never an age or condition you are in that you can't reach and strive to grow from. Be careful of what you expect from yourself as you age because that too will be a self-fulfilling prophecy for the way that you do.

REFUSE TO BELIEVE YOU HAVE LIMITS

As human beings, our tendency is to pull away from the things we think we can't do. If we don't believe we are not good at something, we don't really take that challenge in the same way.

Have a glass ceiling is being contained by an electric fence that's been unplugged for years. It is being contained by a belief that has not basis in your actual ability. You are contained by the belief that you can't just as an animal is controlled by its belief it can't get past the tiny wire that has no real ability to contain it.   .

Because the mental limits in your head are not real, they can't stop you once you get determined not to let them. Glass ceilings are things we shy away from because we believe we can't do them. We don't challenge that electric fence because we believe it. If we did, we would find out that a limit we thought we had was only in our head.

How do you break through your own glass ceilings? You quit approaching your goals tentatively or not at all. We get rid of the back-

Glass ceilings are often a fear of the unknown. Because we fear, and we haven't been that way before, we often stay safely behind a bubble of fear that make us ineffective and breakable.

That fear makes us hyper aware of our struggles and shuts us down and makes us quit when we feel even the slightest physical impulse or resistance in our minds.

Fear makes us hyper ready to quit! When we do, it is usually not our that our bodies reached any real limit in what they can do, but that our heads did.

Most of the limits we think we have are not even real. To shatter our glass ceilings, we simply need to challenge the and get determined to get past them. When we get determined, resilient and intentional about getting past the limits in our head to what we think we can do, we will.

Only quit when your body says quit, not when your mind does. You can't handle the diet when your body can't handle it, not when your mind can't. A limit in your head shouldn't be able to stop you. Make all the physical limits you reach in your life and your body goal be real.

Quit believing and behaving like a person who can't. Instead, start to see yourself as a person who can and will create that amazing makeover. See yourself as a person who accomplishes the things you set your mind on doing and get mentally determined to this.

The glass ceilings that make us ineffective with our bodies and lives are not really limits or things we are not good at all. They are just fear.

Unless you believe and avoid challenging yourself in that area, your mental limits have no power to stop us.

You can do this. You always could. You simply must get determined enough to not let a dumb belief stop you. Don't let your head, or anything else limit what you can do with yourself, your body or your life. Get determined to challenge and defeat every believe you have that says you can't!

THE POWER OF A MAILBOX

The second concept that radically changed the power I had to do this came to me unexpectedly from a mailbox. Understanding the power of a mailbox can help you accomplish a physical goal you haven't been able to achieve any other way.

My mailbox story happened to me clear back in high school, however, it didn't become meaningful or significant to me until much later in my life.

Do you ever feel like life is trying to teach you something?

It did me on that day that I accidently discovered the power of a mailbox.

GET TO THAT MAILBOX

As a kid, I was kind of a geek. School really meant something to me. I didn't have a lot of body confidence, but I did have some academic confidence, and the love of all things learning that often come from it. As a kid, I got a lot of joy from everything school, everything except P.E. that is.

I would read anything I could get my hands on and get so lost in a book that I would lose all track of time. History fascinated me and so did science. I loved math and physics and the bridge I built in physics made it to the state-level bridge building competition. I took the first computer programming class ever taught at my school, and I was the only girl in it. I loved and excelled at art as was nominated for as the top art student in my school one year. Also, because of my interest in math and science, I was even being scouted for a Women in Engineering program the university was promoting to get more girls to go into careers in engineering. Okay, I was a geek! I loved all things learning and disliked and avoided most thing physical when I could.

However, one day, on a school day that was very important to me, although I can't remember why, I missed the bus. Likely, I had project that day or a high stakes test that mattered to me, but for some reason, I felt like I couldn't miss that day that really mattered to me,

Having no other way to get there, I decided to walk. Then, afraid of missing whatever it was, I decided to run as much as I could.

I was so out of shape that I was out of breath by the time I got to the end of driveway.

SET YOUR EYES ON THAT NEXT MAILBOX

That is where I would generally quit. Okay, let's be honest about it. I would normally never start, but that day, just as I was about to quit, I looked up and set my eyes on my neighbor's mailbox which was about 50 feet ahead of where I was at the time.

I'm not sure why, but for some reason I set my eyes on that mailbox and challenged myself to go just a little further than I thought I could to make it to that very next mailbox.

50 feet is not very far to run, but it was farther than I thought I could. However, by setting that tiny stretch goal for myself and putting my focus on getting there, I did it. When I reached that mailbox, a surprising thing happened. I reached that mailbox fully intending to quit, but the boost of confidence and accomplishment I get when I did, made me lift my eyes and set them on the next mailbox.

The boost I got from doing something that was more than I thought I could do made me reach a little deeper and find I still had a little left in the tank, and with that, I set my eyes on that very next mailbox and committed to myself to make it to just one more.

You are probably guessing by now that I did that again, and I did. Of course, I didn't keep that pace up the whole way. After a while, I slipped to more of a run one, walk one pace. Then, realizing I was fine, I would challenge myself to run two of them before I let myself walk again.

Little by little, I used those mailboxes to challenge and encourage myself to school that day. I found the power of a mailbox is that it can get you past something that usually intimidates and psyches you out.

That day I made it to school on my own power. Yes, I was late, but I was also exhilarated to find that I had a way to get past the limits and glass ceilings I had in my head. I was late to school, but to the best of my knowledge, I did make it to the event that was so important to me that day.

More important than that event, however, was that I learned something significant about human nature. You can always go that 50 feet beyond where you think you can, and often when you do you can go a little more.

Our mental barriers stop us from achieving our physical goals far more than our physical ones do, and the way to get past a mental barrier is by not looking at the whole thing. Just challenge yourself to make it to that mailbox that is a little past what you would normally do.

Intimidation is the enemy of our body goals. Intimidation shuts us down before we do anything. To get past our intimidation, we need A TINY CHALLENGE!

I wish I could say that that event changed my life physically, but it didn't, I wish I could say that because of my run with those mailboxes I abandoned all the belief I had that I can't. I wish I had a happily ever-after story to tell you about how I changed my belief in myself that day, but I don't.

I kept right on believing that anomaly was something so foreign and unusual that it was not me. However, at random times in my life, I thought about those mailboxes. That experience running to school that day had a rather random way of popping up for me in my mind.

It took a decade for that learning to percolate and me to understand what life was trying to teach me, but I think, eventually, I did.

MAILBOX GOALS CHALLENGE US PAST INTIMIDATION

From those mailboxes I learned that the best way to get past your fears and intimidation is to focus on that next mailbox!

Mailboxes are the goals that challenge and stretch us just beyond what we think we can do, but not far enough that they stretch into our zone of intimidation.

Mailbox goals are something you must reach a little to do, but not so far that you doubt you can do it. Mailbox goals may be passing that cake without taking a slice. They might be making it to bed tonight with no food after 7. Mailbox goals coax us out of our fears and inch us beyond our intimidation. Yes, sheer determination can break glass ceilings, but so can little by little baby stepping our way beyond them.

Mailbox goals are one of the best ways out there to challenge and get past the Glass Ceilings in our minds that keep us from going places we don't know we can go. The reason they work, of course, is that the limits we think we have are just a mirage. The closer we get to reaching a limit, the further away that limit seems to move.

Most of the time, we sit down and quit when we see that mirage that we think is the limit of what we can do. Trying to get as close to that limit we can't reach as possible is amazingly powerful, because the closer we get, the further away that limit becomes. Like me, when you do a little further than you thought you could, you often look inside and find a little something still left in that tank.

Breaking through the intimation that shuts us down with our body goals is what we must do to get there. One of the best ways to do that is to set your interim goals small and challenge yourself to just get that far.

When I finally made the of decision to lose that weight the decision to do that scared and intimidated me. Maybe that is why it took me so long to make it. Mentally, I couldn't lose a hundred pounds or workout consistently every day. In fact, the thought of a whole workout intimidated me and shut me down. At first, 5 minutes of activity was a good goal. What I found out was that I could do that whole workout in a day if I broke it into 5-minute segments at a time.

Running that first half marathon was so intimidating to me that I hardly slept the night before. That night, those mailboxes invaded my dreams and all at once, understood them. I couldn't let myself see that whole run in my mind. All along that race, there would be a tree, or a sign, or a drink station I could make it to. I could walk when I needed to as long as I challenged myself to go beyond what was easy. The challenge and burst of momentum and encouragement you get from making it to a mailbox you really had to did to make it to, gives you the burst you need to go on from there.

I used to have so much anxiety before I went to the gym to run that I would make myself physically sick as it closer to the end of shift when I went. (later I switched to mornings, which really helped) but every day I expected 3 miles of myself and I did.

Sometimes, that mailbox was just putting on my shoes and getting out the door. Sometimes I had to mentally promise myself I could walk if I ran for 5 minutes. Of course, I often also found that after that 5 minutes I really had to reach for to make, I still had a little more in that tank. Mailbox goals are so powerful because they challenge us past our own resistance.

Losing a hundred pounds was also so intimidating it shut me down. I couldn't fathom losing a hundred pounds or running multiple half marathons like I did. That behavior was so far out of my realm of possibility, so far past my own glass ceiling that setting my sights on doing it shut me down.

For much of that time, I had to put my ultimate goal in the back of my mind and focus on just making it to the very next mailbox. I couldn't focus on losing a hundred pounds, but I could make it to 10 am or bedtime without messing up my eating if I challenged myself to. I could do Keto for a day. I would often find out that I could make it through the whole workout if I mentally challenged myself to at least get through the warm-up on the days when that seemed hard to do.

Those mailboxes life made me focus on in high school became huge to me as a strategy that could help get me past my own glass ceilings and mental limits in my life.

SIDE NOTE: One of the ways I lost that weight was to switch it up by buying one of those weekly magazines that have diets in them and challenging myself to do somewhere between 3 to 5 days of that plan. That strategy helped me kept it fresh when I needed it, and gave me a concrete, reachable mailbox I could focus on in my mind.

COMMIT TO RESULTS, NOT TO A PROCESS

When we commit to a diet, we fail when that diet fails for us. When we commit to a result and we leave the strategy flexible, we can learn and change and adapt as we go.

A diet is just a tool. So is a particular kind of activity or workout. We become too breakable when we commit to a process or way we are going to get there.

When the first tool in your toolbox doesn't work, you try something else. When we fail at a diet, or the gym is not working for us, we often get discouraged and quit.

Mailboxes are powerful because you can switch up your strategy as you lose each of those pounds or change that activity as you get bored or need something different.

Your ultimate goal is your commitment to that result. Keep an open mind and a willingness to be flexible with the way you get there as you go. Flexibility of process allows you to avoid that discouragement that shuts you down when one thing you try doesn't work.

Keep your process flexible. Don't set yourself up for failure when the first tool you try doesn't work. This is a learning experience as well. Try a lot of strategies with one requirement, they get you where you want to be. Allowing myself to be flexible at times and fixed at others worked well for me. I just needed a short-term goal, like a day or a week or a pound or time I could focus myself on reaching.

MAILBOXES GET US PAST HUNGER

I couldn't handle being hungry all day (and that's not healthy anyway.) I could challenge myself to accept a little hunger and let myself reach it before I ate my next meal. I could challenge myself to eat lightly enough that I would be a little hungry by the time I went to bed.

The same is the of cravings. I couldn't handle never eating that food again in my mind, but I could handle delaying a craving for the 20 minutes it takes for most cravings to go away. 20 minutes is a great mailbox to see if your hunger is real or a craving will go away on its own.

20 minutes is a good mailbox of time that will help get us past the hunger and cravings that gets in our way. To use it, make it a policy to drink some water and wait 20 minutes when you want to eat.

MAILBOXES GET US THROUGH WORKOUTS

When I started running, I had to commit to just putting on those shoes and getting out the door every day, not knowing how much I would do when I did or if I would walk or run most of it. Mentally, I had to commit to putting on those shoes and getting out the door every day. Mentally, those shoes were my mailbox.

Our own intimidation is the enemy of our fitness goals and journey. We simply need a strategy that will get us past our own intimidation. That strategy is having a mailbox goal to get us started. Whether that is putting on your fitness clothes, tying up your fitness shoes or challenging yourself to just make it through the warmup or first 5 minutes.

Ultimately, I committed to climb to the top of the highest mountain in our and as I stood on that peak, looking down both sides of into the valleys below, I area realized, I have no limits. I must get past intimidation in my own mind that shut me down.

Glass ceilings are built out of fear and intimidation. We don't think we can, so we don't. Mailbox goals challenge us through our intimidation and before you know it, we prove that we don't really have that limit at all.

Mailbox goals combined with determination, shatter glass ceilings. They do so by giving us a concrete goal that challenges us beyond our normal, but not so far into the zone of intimidation in our mind that shuts us down.

SET A MAILBOX GOAL FOR YOURSELF

- Challenge yourself to eat perfectly for three successful days in a row!
- Challenge yourself to working out for seven consecutive days.
- Challenge yourself to run and/or or walk for 30 straight minutes.
- If you can't challenge yourself to give up sugar completely, put a limit on it. Count your grams and try to improve it.
- Challenge yourself to postpone your hunger and cravings for 20 minutes when you feel them.
- Challenge yourself to drink some water and wait 20 minutes to get control over your own impulse.

Often, by challenging yourself to wait just 20 minutes before you comply to a craving or your hunger, you gain control over your own impulse and get control over your eating so you can achieve your goals.

BREAK IT DOWN

If a mailbox doesn't work and something still intimidates you, break it down even more. Does five minutes intimidate you? Then commit to do just one minute of that workout. Commit to distract yourself for five minutes while you are waiting for a craving to subside.

All big accomplishments that we think we can't do are composed of little things and moments that we can make it to if we try. Challenge yourself to go on a walk, skip carbs at dinner, give up soda for today or something else that will get you one step closer to where you want to be in the end.

Don't let your head put a limit on the things your body can do.

MAKE ALL YOUR PHYSICAL LIMITS REAL

Use mailbox goals to challenge yourself past your own intimidation to reach level of accomplishment you never thought that you could achieve! Mailbox goals shatter the glass ceilings in your mind so you can!

CHAPTER

FOUR

WHO ARE YOU IN THAT MENTAL MIRROR?

Everything you do goes according to a view you have of yourself or something else in your head. All your behavior comes from the mental blueprint you have of who you are.

Change your mental blueprint by changing a view of who you are or how you see something, and you change your reality.

Sometimes the reason you struggle with your body is because of a mental image you have of who you are and the way you feel about food and fitness in your head.

Your self-concept is too important to let it be counterproductive to your

Sometimes the reason we don't do better with our bodies is we don't see ourselves that way. When we mentally become a person, who doesn't have the willpower or we don't see ourselves as a person who works out or eats right in our minds, it changes the things we think and do. All too often, when we eat badly or don't work out, we are living consistently with a mental picture we have of who we are.

Our mental image of us is perhaps the most important thing we have because it determines who we strive hard to be. We will work so hard to stay consistent with our own mental image that the way we see ourselves as a physical person drives how we eat, think, feel and all the things that we do.

Our mental image of ourselves is critical because it drives our expectations, and we will work very hard or meltdown into a huge mess based on the image we see in our own mental mirror. In many ways, ask yourself, "Who am I in my own picture of myself? Who am I in my own head?" Make sure that image you have of who you are is computable with who you want to be.

Sometimes, we just can't accomplish our physical goals because of the way we see ourselves as a physical person in our mind. We don't yet hold ourselves to that expectation every day because it is not yet the way we see ourselves.

Before, or more accurately during this process of change, we are challenging a mental of ourselves and how we eat and what we can physically do in our heads. We are not just changing on the outside, we must also change our own view of ourselves until we see ourselves as a person who loves to be active and who eats right every day.

When we modify our image of who we are and let ourselves become a person who works out or likes to be active, or someone who can walk past that cake to stay on track, we become a person who can and who does on the outside as well. Sometimes, it is the image of a person who doesn't have the willpower to constantly stay on track or who doesn't like to workout that is making us act the way we do.

YOUR SELF-IMAGE IS YOUR MENTAL BLUEPRINT

Really, every day, we are simply living up to or down to a mental image we have of ourselves in our heads. We are simply living up to or down to our own expectation. The words, 'This is me. This is who I am' are so powerful, that they become the mental blueprint for everything we do. When you accept something into an image you have of yourself, you work hard to stay true to that image, regardless of whether it is hard or it hurts.

We MUST strive to live true to that mental image we have of ourselves in that mirror. We put in tremendous effort to achieve our own high expectations or we meltdown to tremendously low place to stay consistent with our low ones. We MUST live consistently with the way we see ourselves in that mirror. We do this even it takes years of striving, or other people don't see us that way.

That image that makes us something special or tells us we are less than enough is the blueprint for how we live and who we are going to be. If we see ourselves as effective and determined, we will be. If we see negative traits in that mental mirror, we self-destruct to match that image as well. Whether good or bad, the person we see in that mental mirror in our heads, will drive the way strive with our bodies or meltdown with our willpower and justification for failure as well.

WE HAVE AN IMAGE OF OURSELVES PHYSICALLY

We don't just have one mental mirror. In fact, we have many.

When I look in my intellectual or educational mirror, I see a different person than I do when I see everything that defines who I think I physically am.

I have a different view of myself in that mirror of who I am as a mother or a grandmother, than I do in the mirror of myself as an artist, or (heaven help us) a singer. I have a view of myself as a teacher or as a writer or a hundred other contexts I could see myself in. In each case, the image I have of myself in that mirror shape the person I will be in that part of my life.

Well, of course, you have an image of who you think you are physically as well. The way you see yourself, your direction, ability and even your determination to do something physically will determine how you eat and what you do in your life physically.

Are you a person who can walk past that cake? Are you a person who will accomplish this goal? If not, you may need to become one in your mind.

YOUR MAY HAVE TO CHANGE YOUR VIEW OF YOURSELF

Sometimes, it is the way we see ourselves and our physical behavior in that mental mirror that is behind the whole problem we have with our bodies and our physical goals. We see ourselves as a person who eats like this. So, we do. we don't see ourselves as a person who can stay on track. So, we don't!

How do you see yourself as a physical person? Who do you see in your physical mental mirror?

Do you see a person who spirals out of control or one determined to stay on track? Do you see a top athlete who never gives up? Do you see an active person who will get out there, or one prefers to sit on the couch?

> *To accomplish your physical goal, you MUST quit being that fat person who doesn't have any self-control in your head!*

We behave consistently with that person we believe ourselves to be. We live true to that image we have of ourselves in our minds whether that vision inspires or destroys us. Our mental image of who we are is perhaps the most important thing we have because it is the blueprint for everything we do in our lives. Our mental image of who we are becomes the blueprint for who we will become and how we will live both physically and personally in our lives.

We MUST be aware of and respect the power of the image we have of ourselves in our head.

Few of us realize that the problems we have sticking with and accomplishing our physical goals come from the way we see ourselves in that area of our lives. We don't know we have a physical identity to begin with, so we have NO CHANCE of looking at how we see ourselves physically or deciding if that image is good for us and in line with our goals.

We can't fix our mental image of ourselves as a person who has willpower and does because we don't even know we have a view of ourselves physically that might be working against us.

Often, it is only the hurtful and self-defeating views we have of ourselves that are hurting us. Sometimes, to get to better place, be they physically, mentally, or emotionally, we just must take a look at the person we are allowing ourselves to be in our own mental mirror and fix it!

Our mental image of ourselves works when our views are positive, they inspire high expectations, and they lead us where we want to be. Our views of who we are negative, frustrating, and hurtful, when we think we see ourselves as defective or less than we want to be.

When the way you see yourself or something else shuts you down or makes you ineffective or miserable, it is time to change the way you see that thing.

> **"We can't solve our problems by using the same kind of thinking we used to create them."**
>
> **~ Albert Einstein**

Your mental image is the blueprint for all your behavior and emotion. It determines everything about how you live and how you feel. That image you have in your mental mirror will determine whether you are wildly successful at what you do or not.

How do you see yourself in your own physical mental mirror? Are you fit? Are you able? Are determined to reach the goals you set for yourself? Are you willing to modify your views of who you are physically to let yourself mentally become something else?

You don't have to jump to

being a top athlete in your head.

You do need to get to start seeing yourself

as getting on track and being a person

who is going in the right direction.

You will never become fit and effective at your body goal, until you are willing to at least work on changing the views you have of yourself in that mental mirror. You must let yourself become, not just on the outside. You must modify the views you have of who you are physically and the way you see yourself in the mental mirror on the inside as well.

Don't allow yourself to see the person you are in any hurtful or depowering ways. Your mental image of your is perhaps the most important thing you have, and it is completely your creation.

CHOOSE YOUR VIEW

Your perception of yourself affects literally everything you think, do, and feel. You MUST get more aware of and responsible for the views you have of you. That mental image you have of you, along with your perception of your life and the people and things around you, have tremendous effect on your energy, your power, your emotion, and your effectiveness in everything that you do. You must *Actively choose the views you allow yourself to have of you!*

If you want to be fit, strong and healthy in the actual mirror, you need to become fit, strong, healthy, and determined in that mental mirror in your head. Mentally become a person who can and who will. Mentally see yourself in ways that help you accomplish the things that you really want to do.

THE LAWS OF HUMAN BEHAVIOR

If I could propose one LAW OF HUMAN BEHAVIOR that trumps them all, it would be this:

We must behave consistently with the way

we see ourselves in our own mental mirror.

Our mental mirror is the blueprint for all our human behavior and emotion. Therefore, the image you have of yourself in your own mental mirror, the way you see yourself, is perhaps your most important creation.

If you have struggled with your body or your body goals or been ineffective at losing weight and getting fit in the past, it is likely you have been performing according to a view you have of yourself and your physical performance in your head. Are you really seeing yourself as a person who can and will and does? If not, you may have to change that.

CHANGE THE EXPECTATIONS YOU HAVE

FOR YOUR PHYSICAL BEHAVIOR IN YOUR HEAD

BECOME SOMETHING NEW PHYSICALLY

WHEN YOU SEE YOURSELF IN YOUR HEAD

That magic mirror of self-image is SO POWERFUL that the image of the person you see in yours, physically, and in every other way, will determine the one you work to become in your life.

See yourself as a fit and healthy person who has high physical expectations of yourself in life. See yourself as someone who is so determined to get someone physically that you will do whatever it takes to get this done. Become the person you want to be in your own mental mirror, and you will become that person for real in the rest of your life.

GET FIT AND EFFECTIVE IN YOUR MENTAL MIRROR

AND YOU WILL IN YOUR LIFE AS WELL

LOSING THE WEIGHT AND KEEPING IT OFF

When I look back at the pictures of myself as a young person, I wasn't really all that heavy, but I was in my head. I look back at those pics of myself then and I think, "What was the big deal? I was fine!" It was only in my head that I was too heavy and out of shape.

Sadly, those views I had of myself shaped my behavior until that person I saw in the mirror was eventually to one I became. My bad body image, and the non-physical image I had of myself and my likes and dislikes shaped my behavior until my physical body became consistent with the way I saw things in my own mental mirror.

That mental mirror we have of who we are physically, and what we like and cand do shapes who we physically become. Even after losing weight or getting fit, if we don't change that image of who we are physically, we are very prone to spiral back to it when we are not vigilant or something in the life we had planned goes wrong. Our self-image and the expectations we have of what we do with ourselves and our bodies makes our behavior stable and makes us consistently perform that way we do. If we are not vigilant about our self-image, we are very prone to return to the behavior and weight that is consistent with who we 'really' think ourselves to be.

Unless we modify our self-image to go with that weight loss, those change we made will be very fragile in our lives. Until we modify these unhealthy views of the 'real person' we are in our heads and mentally become a person who lives like this, and who now is this way, we will be very prone to falling back to image of how we see ourselves naturally behave in that mirror. We MUST change our views of who we are on the inside to permanently change on the outside as well.

Make your mental image in that mirror one of competence,

kindness, strength, vision, and effectiveness so you can be that in life

You can't be that fat kid with no willpower

in your head and expect to be anything else

in your life or your body.

We MUST behave consistently with the person we see ourselves to be. Therefore, let yourself become the fit and happy person who eats healthy is active and enjoys in that life in your mind so you can do that in your life.

BUT DON'T EXPECT EITEHR YOUR MENTAL OR PHYSICL MAKEOVERS TO BE INSTANT

Change takes time. Changing the way you see yourself is a gradual process. Don't expect your mental or physical makeovers to happen instantly. You are slowly becoming better in body and mind. It took years for you to build the self-image that you have, just as it likely took years to get where you physically are.

Have patience in the changes you have for you body and for things you are changing about yourself and the process.

Your mindset and your view of you are always evolving. If you let them, your views of yourself and the things around you will keep getting better and better. You are refining and shaping your mindset just as you are refining and shaping your body

You are a work on art both inside and out. You may still be a work of art in progress, but you are a work of art. See yourself that way, and be patient with the time it takes to build and create yourself. Great works of art take time. You are becoming that masterpiece you want to be in you body and mind. Be patient with yourself as you do.

Have a goal of continual self-improvement. We should be growing and getting better every day of our lives, regardless of our age.

You are mentally and physically evolving toward that vision you have of who you are and who you have decided to be. don't lose sight of that vision or the determination to keep working toward it, but don't' expect that change to be instant either.

INTENTIONALLY AND SYSTEMATICALLY

Create a vison of yourself as the person you want to be.

When you look in that mirror see a person who is, who can,

who does and who refuses to stop until they are.

I'M STILL WORKING ON MY IMAGE OF ME

I've come a long way from the way I saw myself in the past, to the way I see myself and my ability now, but at times, I still slip back there in my mind. Luckily, these days, I can recognize and effectiveness and reality check that view much quicker than I used to, but don't assume that because I'm writing the book that I've always got a handle on my mental image either.

I'm still working on me. I am working on who I am both inside and out. Being diligent about my own mental image is something I will have to do for life. Let the mental image you have of yourself change, but it is a process. Don't expect to instantly see that person you want to be looking back at you in the mirror of who you are in your mind.

YOU ARE EVOLVING A SELF-IMAGE!

Let that person you see in that mental mirror continue to change and to grow. See yourself as getting more fit and having more willpower and ability than you used to have. Don't have a fixed mindset about who you are or what you do physically. Stay flexible about your view of you.

Don't paint yourself into a corner of behavior by thinking 'this is who I am.' Growth and change in the purpose of existence and you won't grow or change if you think, 'this is who I am.'

Don't let yourself mentally be a person who can't. Don't allow a negative or fixed identity. It's not accurate It is not healthy and it's not you. Life is not about where you are now. You are not identified or limited by a current direction or level of functioning. Life is about growth.

We don't stay in one place mentally or physical unless we refuse to change who we are in our minds. Methodically, let the person who looks back at you in that mirror become closer to the person you want to be both inside and out.

SHAPE AND ABILITY-ISM

Part of the pain we do to ourselves when we are physically out of shape or going in the wrong direction is because of the judgmental views society has about shape-ism.

Along with all the other divisive in our world, we humans, often sees people who are not in good physical shape in ways that are hurtful to them and divisive for us all.

Our world has been working on divisive views, like racism and sexism for a long time now. We often don't recognize or do anything about another form of prejudice that is very hurtful and nearly invisible. That prejudice is shape-ism. One of the reasons it personally hurts us so badly to be out of shape is that we feel the weight of all the silent judgmental and hurtful views our society has of people who are overweight or out of shape. .

Like other 'blame the victim' prejudice (poverty, unemployment, or homelessness, etc.) people who are outside the social norm of size and shape are often judged harshly because we it as a personal flaw. Many of negative stereo types our world has about weight and physical condition come with elements of shame and of blame that badly that cut us to the core when we are the person who falls on the wrong side.

One reason we see ourselves so badly when we are overweight or out of shape is because society does.

Shame and blame just don't work well as motivators of changing our bodies. We already do far too much shame and blame of ourselves and it just takes away our power when we do.

Like all other ways of dividing people, shape-ism takes away the power and respect and belief in our own ability we need to see each other for empowerment and real communication. People who are overweight or obese are often not given our full respect, and those of us who are overweight are as guilty of that as anyone else. We see it as a character flaw and for judgement of ourselves and other based on shape as well. .

This prejudice makes us devalue those who are heavy and devalue or demean ourselves when we are. We make heavy people disappear when we speak to them. We become invisible ourselves when we don't think we are enough or we have what it takes for physical change.

Size so gets in the way of connection. We don't seriously hear the opinions of those above the norms of size when we let size gets in the way. Even characters who are overweight on TV or in movies are often seen as flat, out of control characters who don't have strength and are defined by a weakness of lack of control with food.

While we have worked hard to remove many other prejudices from our media, our prejudice about weight and shape is demeaning all around us

THIS INVISIBLE PREJUDICE THAT IS KEEPING US FAT

This invisible prejudice affects the way we see ourselves in ways that take away the power we need to fix it.

As a child, I felt fundamentally different from fit people in my mind. My social learning even helped me justify a divide between myself and those of us who were 'born to be fit and look good' on the other side. Physically, I felt fundamentally different.

This encouraged sour grapes and the devaluing and judging the other side we often do to help balance that equation.

For example, my family, and many others saw fit people as people who spend too much time and attention on their look. Therefore, they are naturally shallow. You could be beautiful on the outside OR you be a beautiful person on the inside, but not both! Division almost always comes with judgement that attempts to balance the equation in our minds.

In our world, being heavy or out of shape comes with judgement that hurts and weaken us all. "If I am fat, I must be weak. Because I am fat, I don't have willpower. My shape and condition prove that I am not strong or fit and that I can't. We sometimes invisibly judge the other side negatively as well, (think gym rats, or mean girls.)

Falling on the deficit side of some social norms, especially one we should be able to fix, almost always comes with some guilt and some pain, but sometimes it also come with some self-esteem saving justification o judgment the other side that can get in our way when we try to change as well. Our minds do all kind of things to us in an attempt to protect our all-important self-esteem. Make sure you don't see some element of bad in the very thing you are trying to become.

DIVISION IS NORMAL

Humans divide themselves into groups. As bad as that is, it is also a product of our very intelligent minds. Because of our intelligence, our human minds like to sort and categories things in our heads. It is a natural side effect of being human to separate and categorize ourselves and everything else into groups.

As humans we sort and categorize things into groups based on similarity and difference all the time. From the time we are little, kids separating animals into 'barnyard' or 'zoo' animals. They sort crayons and candies into piles by color and by size. As bad as it is, it is quite natural that humans sort each other into artificial categories by many attributes in our heads.

Sorting and classifying may be a normal part of intelligence, but it is also a lower-level intellectual skill. Just as we incorrectly separate, we must actively reality check and put things that shouldn't be separated back together in our heads. It is a higher-level skill to look at our division and intentionally put it back together than it is to separate ourselves mentally in our head in the first place.

We all know divisions is inaccurate, and hurtful for us all. The worst part of separating into categories is that is separates us from some of our human resource and it stops the authentic connection and communication we need to have between us all.

An overweight or obese person needs to bring down their 'fit person' walls, just as those who are fit need to bring down the walls that makes separates them from those who are not. People of all sizes and conditions need to take down the walls of judgment that separates them from seeing and connecting with each other authentically. Recognition that we have mentally divided is always the first step toward fixing it. We must see prejudice about shape and condition before we can bring down yet another wall that divides and separates us as human beings in our minds.

COACHING WORKS

The thing that makes coaching work is real and authentic communication. To get there, we often have to bring down some walls on both sides. Before we can really get coaching or be an effective coach, we must bring down the walls that narrow the gaps between us. Real and authentic connection is the key to effective coaching. We must start seeing people on both sides of the weight and shape authentically so we can get and give the help we need.

Coaching can't be one strong side and one that is weak the way we think it is.

There is strength on both sides of any authentic communication and coaching MUST be real authentic communication for it to work at its best. Real coaching needs transparent sharing. It begins with a trusting, helping relationships that sees both strength and weakness on both sides.

Real coaching breaks down the walls between us. It helps us authentically connect and lets us benefit from the knowledge of us all. Real coaching lets up open our struggles and authentically share the strength and weakness of both sies.

Coaching gives us accountability with someone who cares and has a vested interest in our success. Coaches pull us up when we are down, celebrate with us when we do something right, guide us into what to do next and build us up so we can get when we want to be.

Coaches take us by the hand and help us get to places we often can't get to without their help.

SHARE YOUR JOURNEY WITH COACHING

No matter which side of your body journey you are on, consider reaching out for coaching or becoming a coach yourself. Coaching is sharing this journey with someone else. It is being vesting or having , someone vested in getting you where you want to go. The things that are now so simple, or at least so manageable for some of us still seem so hard or nearly impossible for others. When you cross a bridge, or if you need to, consider reaching back or ahead with coaching yourself or someone else across cross that great divide.

ONE MORE WISH of mine (as a writer, I can throw wishes to the universe because who knows where they might land) is that coaching of all types was more easily available. I would love to see coaching for kids in poverty. Someone who has been that way themselves could mentally and physically coach a kid through school and registering for college, and even on into work, career, and life. A program like a digital Big Brothers and Sisters program could let some people give back easily while give kids who don't have that experience at home get the support they need.

Coaching works and I'm a big believer in it, because of the support and connection it brings down walls and creates real change. Sometimes, it takes other eyes on a situation, and other ideas, accountability, and celebration to take a hand to get us where we want to be.

We all need help out of some box and we all can help someone get out of theirs. Be it financial, obesity, fitness, a life choice, or weight loss with help we can get out of the boxes we are in that contain us.

OUR VISION FOR OUR WEBSITE IS TO OPEN IT UP TO MORE DIVERSE TYPES OF COACHING. IF WE DON'T, AND EVEN IF WE DO, OUR WORLD NEEDS MORE ACCESSIBLE COACHING.

COACHING WORKS WHEN WE BUILD OUR TRUST AND OUR AUTHENTIC COMMUNICATION ON BOTH SIDES.

(Check out our coaching site www.coachifyme.com if you want to become a coach or get Body Mindset certified or find a coach that can help you accomplish a wide variety of personal or body goals.)

YOU BODY GOALS CANNOT BE JUST ABOUT YOUR LOOKS

In our minds there must be no doubt that health and fitness matters and that it adds benefit to us and our lives right now, not just in the future.

Too many of us do this for our looks. Well, our looks don't make the cut of a real priority. Maybe they do while we are young, or while we are looking for a spouse, but the motivation of looking good is naturally temporary. We need a motivation that is deeper and more substantial than looks.

What else does living in a physically healthy way bring to your life?

> ➢ A healthy lifestyle brings power and energy to your life!
> ➢ You get more powerful and effective in everything you do. Power breeds power. Competence in your physical goals breeds competence in all the other areas as well.
> ➢ Perhaps the most important reason to take care of your body the way you should is that healthy living affects emotion.
> ➢ It changes the way you feel about you, which radiates power, positive emotion, and self-esteem into the rest of our lives in a way that affects nearly everything else.
> ➢ When you take care of your body competently, you feel the joy, and a sense of accomplishment and being on top of things that you can get in no other way.

- Living a healthy life gives you an energy and power and a burst of good emotion.
- Quality of life! There is no doubt that healthy living will give you the quality of life that you want to have right now.
- Sure, fitness and healthy eating will make you LOOK BETTER, but looks are not really the point. The point is, feeling good, being stronger and getting more personally powerful. Yes, you get better looks, but looks are not the point. (Think of them as kind of a FREE GIFT for living that healthy life you should .)

There is no downside to choosing to eat right and workout every day. . Fitness and self-care improve your moods, your power, and your self-esteem. My mom would have had 20 more years of quality in her life if she could have gotten her health and her weight under control. She didn't need to have all that depression and stress and negative feelings she had about her weight.

There is no doubt in my mind, and there must be no doubt in yours, that there are no negatives to self-care!

Taking care of your body right and eating right every day improves your energy. It improves your mental sharpness. It increases your length of life and the quality in your years. It improves your mood and make you better able to handle your life and relate well to the people around you. And as a FREE GIFT, you also get to look better on the outside as well. Taking care of your body improves your life and makes you more beautiful both inside and out because you act and feel better mentally and physically when you feel good about you.

TO GET BETTER AT DOING IT

MAKE IT MATTER MORE

TO YOU IN YOUR HEAD

CHAPTER
FIVE

UNDER THE INFLUENCE

*We never make our best decisions when we
are under the influence of negative emotion.*

O ften, it is the battle we have with our own emotion
that distracts us from our body goals. One of the
solutions to gaining control of our eating and
becoming effective with our body goals is often
learning to get better at managing and choosing our
own emotion.

When we combined our own better emotional control with a way to protect our goals from the inevitable times, we are under that emotional weather in our lives, so we don't destroy our progress when we are, we become tremendously more effective at staying on track and achieving our goals.

Emotional self-regulation is often the key to staying on a better physical track.

UNDER THE INFLUENCE OF NEGATIVE EMOTION

We never make our best decisions when we are under the influence of negative emotion. Those of us who overeat know that the eating we do when we are under the influence of negative emotion is devastating for our body goals. Therefore, better control of our own emotions is critical to getting control of our body and our goals.

We all have good physical intentions, unless we have reached such a low spot with it that we have given up. Most of us have good intentions. We set good body goals and make effective plan that can get us there. Then, we get side raided by our own emotion and emotion laden excuses that excuse us from staying on track.

It is often emotion that gets our heads out of the 'right place' and makes us lose focus and direction a goal we want to pursue.

Staying on track with ANY GOAL requires that we learn how to manage and regulate the negative emotion that could get us wrapped up into loops of anger or self-pity in our heads.

While it may not seem like it, learning to control your emotion is one of the most important components of learning to control your eating and accomplish your body goals.

YOUR SELF CONTROL IS AFFECTED BY EMOTION

Deciding to get in a better emotional place in your life will give you more power over your willpower and self-control. Choosing how to see something in your life dramatically affects the way you feel, which affect your control of you.

WE ALL KNOW that emotional eating often sabotages our body goals. It just makes sense that better controlling our own emotion will help us better control the eating that depends on it.

By choosing your mindset about some of the challenges and daily struggles of your life, you get control over how far to let those things take you down. We often mistakenly believe that emotion something that happens to us. We often believe we have no control over the emotion that so often is in control of us. After all, who would choose to feel a negative emotion if they don't have to?

But we do have control of our own emotions. We get control of them when we get better control of the repeating thoughts that cause them. An emotion is caused, not only by our views and interpretations of things in our lived, but by which thoughts we allow to play and run on automatic loops in our heads,

CHANGE THE CHANNEL ON NEGATIVE EMOTION

We don't always think we have control over our emotions, and once we get fully flooded with the chemicals of that negative emotion, we may not get that out of our system of awhile.

The key to controlling that emotion, is we need to not click on those pop-up ads for negative things to think in our minds and change the channel on the thought that automatically pop into our heads.

It is not those random little options of negative things to think that hurt us. We all get them. It the advertisement for a mental path to follow that you click and get stuck on and that emotionally charged thought you let play on repeat, building and intensifying that emotion every time you do.

Th secret key to staying in control

of your own emotion is this:

Emotion is not created by that first thought.

Negative emotion is built up into a force that can take us down by a negative charged thought we allow to spiral and build up negative emotional energy with every repetition in your head.

THE SPIRALING THOUGHTS OF EMOTION

Like electricity, those negative, or positive emotions gain power when they loop and spin around in our heads. Negative emotional energy is not generated by a single, fleeting thought. It is built by the high or low, underlying level of negative thoughts we allow to loop and spin on auto-play through our heads.

We get control of our emotion, by changing the channel every time we recognize we are thinking a thought that is negative.

One negative thought, that we get rid of quickly, doesn't hurt us. We all have them. Those are as common and predictable as the ads that pop up on our computer. Just because you have the option to see yourself, someone else or the situation as negative, however, doesn't mean you have to 'click' on that option and pursue it.

You don't watch every show that is advertised for you to see. Seeing that trailer in your mind, doesn't mean you need to click on and watch that whole negative energy generating show.

THE ELECTRICITY OF EMOTION

Electricity is the flow of electrons that happens with when a magnet is spun repeatedly inside some loops of wire. Spinning electrically or in this case, emotionally charged thoughts in loops in your mind generates the and intensifies the energy inside them.

It's not just negative emotion that is generated by repetition. Try spinning your thoughts of gratitude around until you work them into a frenzy of overwhelming gratefulness. It is a powerful experience.

 Remember that romantic obsession, you had when you were young, or maybe even last week. You didn't just think about that person once. You spun those emotionally charged thoughts up until you worked them into a frenzy of obsession in your head. If it was a real obsession, the thoughts of that person permeated your head until your worked yourself up into a romantic obsession that made you obsess about that person. One option of something to think doesn't create emotion. Taking the bait on that thought and watching that emotionally charged show does.

like other mind-altering chemicals, emotion affects our control of ourselves. We get control of our emotion by deciding which thought to purse and how long we will pursue and follow them down into that rabbit hole of negative emotion in our lives.

SELF-CONTROL BEGINS WITH OUR EMOTION

Our willpower, and every other kinds of self-control comes from our ability to get control of ourselves and our own emotion. Self-control begins with our own internal emotional regulation.

NEGATIVE THOUGHTS ARE ADDICTING

No one is sure why negative emotion and self-pity is so addicting, but we are very tempted to click into those 'poor me' thoughts that pop up in our heads. Maybe it is a way to get our own personal attention. Maybe we love the pity of it because it is like being coddled and fussed over by our parents when we get hurt. Maybe it gives us an excuse to get out of things we don't want to do. Of course, drama in general is addicting, but avoiding the temptation to click into our own pain and drama and spend some time in that often takes a little self-control.

NOTE: THE MORE YOU AVOID SELF PITY AND NEGATIVE EMOTION, THE EASIER IT GETS AND THE BETTER YOU GET AT IT.

Self-pity and negativity are habits we must get conscious of to break.

Luckily, emotion is easier to manage than we think it is. We just must choose to not follow and pursue a negative thought that could cause it. .

The winds of emotion that blow us back and forth in our lives make it hard to stay on track with our diets, our body goals or anything else. Until we also work to get and keep our emotions under control, we will have a hard time staying on track with our diets and our body goals long enough to achieve them.

BAD THINGS HAPPEN TO GOOD PEOPLE

Of course, emotional regulation won't take away the very real things that happen to us in our lives. Bad things happen to good people. We know that! Emotional management doesn't mean only good things will happen to us. It doesn't mean that things will be easy, or life will be fair. It gives us choice for how far down we let that take us. Bad things happened to good people and they always will because they happen to us all.

Those bad times will require more diligence from us to stay in a reasonably good place. It is okay to sink into our pain to grieve and to heal, but we can't stay down there forever.

Bad things require that we get more diligent in how we see and interpret those things. They require that we intentionally reframe things and find a new way to see them in our heads. They often require that we make change or find our power within them, but by doing so, we will bob back to the surface and get ourselves back under better emotional control. Just because bad things happen, we don't have to follow those things down the rabbit hole of our own demise.

Bad things happen to good people. Good people reframe them the best they can and try to find balance within them the best that they can.

Our resilience amid the bad and hard things in our lives is one of the most amazing things that humans can do. We have the ability to bounce back with resilient even from the most negative of times and events.

When bad things happen to you, you must make the active choice to change course in your mind when you need to, but don't let this, or anything else, keep you down for long.

DON'T ALLOW UNHEALTHY
FOODS TO BE IN YOUR BODY, OR
UNHEALTHY THOUGHTS TO BE
IN YOUR HEAD.

The Body Mindset

CHAPTER
SIX

THE POWER OF INSTANT EMOTIONAL REWARD

T he absolute best reward you can give yourself or anyone else for doing the things they should is the reward of instant positive emotion when they do. Reward yourself for your good body behavior by instantly letting yourself instantly feel good emotionally when you do.

Feeling good is all any of us really want. We do the things we do because we either think they will make us happy now, or happy in the future. Our most natural motivation is happiness because all other motivation is for things, we think it will take to get happiness or at least avoidance of pain. The most natural and powerful motivator in the world is emotion. It is powerful because it is already why we do the things we do.

Our desire to feel joy and positive emotion and avoid feeling bad is the real motivation behind EVERYTHING that we do. Knowing that, you can improve the motivation you have for anything you do by rewarding that things with a glowing internal joy at quickly as you can when you do.

We lose weight because we think it will make us happy and keep us from feeling bad about ourselves and our behavior. We seek money, education, and relationships because we think these things will make us happy. We even do the bad things that we do because we either think they will make us happy, or they will temporarily make us feel better. We want money and relationships and everything else that we do for one reason. We really want happiness! We want to feel happy and good about ourselves. Therefore, the reward that will always be the best human motivator is positive emotion.

When you reward, even your baby steps in the right direction with that reward that we all need and want, you reinforce and strengthen that behavior in yourself. When fitness makes you feel good or passing by that cake gives you a burst of pride that you did, then you just rewarded going in the right direction in a way that will reinforce it.

We often think that our body goals are something we do for a benefit we want in the future. Many people even tell u that the key to maturity is to step over the dime of that instant reward we want right now so we can go for the bigger payoff we want more in the future.

We all want to feel good, and we all want it now. That is why it is why that cake is hard to say no to. The draw of an instant emotional reward is intensely powerful. Even if we know we will get more happiness out of a long-term choice, the desire to feel even a little bit of it now is hard to resist. The draw of instant happiness or instant pain relief is so powerful it is hard to get past. I don't c if you are young or old, we all want that instant reward and we want it now.

Knowing how powerfully we are drawn to feeling good, makes us see the power of the only real motivator in our lives in a way that lets us use it to get both the long and short-term win.

The right things need to make us feel really good right now!

We think of Western Culture as the ones who are most drawn to an instant reward. Really, however, that drive for an instant reward is human nature. It may be easier in some cultures to get that instant reward, but the desire to feel good and get what you want right now is human nature. It is also human nature that what we all really want is to be happy and feel good about ourselves.

Do you really think that cavemen would bypass the quick and easy berries or simple small kill over the big hunt they would need to pursue until tomorrow? Of course not, they ate the berries they found today and went on that big hunt when they needed to tomorrow.

Every culture and time is programed with the drive for instant reward. It is very hard to avoid an instant reward right now to go for a long-term reward we want in the future.

Whether you are training a dog, or a child or yourself, the quicker that reward is tied to the actual behavior, the more powerful the motivation there will be to do it.

That means that by the way we look at them, our body goals are naturally prone to failure. The drive the instant reward of that cake is right there within reach, while that body we want is month of hard work away. Sure, we want it more, but the pull of that instant reward is often just too strong.

We are an INSTANT REWARD SOCIETY

It is not that Western society likes instant reward more than anyone, it is that we are so spoiled by having it that we are not very good at playing the long game to get a bigger reward we have to wait and work to feel in the future.

In our modern world, things have gotten even worse because we are spoiled with instant reward.

Businesses know the power of instant reward. If Amazon can get our package to us faster, or McDonald's can give us quicker food, they know they will take the lion's share of the market because we have even less tolerance for wait than we have in the past.

FIND A DIFFERENT INSTANT REWARD

Our traditional approach has been to train people to get more mature and get better at stepping over the short-term reward to wait for the long-term reward we want more in the future.

Guess what? That approach doesn't work very well!

Sure, we want that better body more than we want that chocolate cake or pizza now. The problem is the proximity of the reward. We can get a short-term payoff now with that cake or pizza or we can get the body we want in six months of bypassing the short-term reward we want to receive. Our body goals often get killed by the power of the instant reward we could experience now.

A MODERN MOTIVATIONAL APPROACH

Luckily, there is a more modern, motivational approach that is grounded in better behavioral science. If we are programed to be drawn toward that instant payoff, then we need to find an instant payoff in the things that we do.

Luckily, there is a lot of intrinsic, instant reward.

We get from taking care of our bodies the way we should.

We need to get into the mindset to recognize, anticipate, and expect that instant emotional payoff when we eat right or workout the way we should. We will get motivated, when we intentionally pay ourselves for doing it now with a flood of positive emotion for doing it when we do.

When we realize that the reward is not just six months in advance, it is now. We can BUILD AN INSTANT REWARD into the things we do well right now. Not only do we get that inherent shot of adrenaline we get from that workout, we can also let ourselves feel really good about it ourselves for doing it when we do. The real reward of that healthy lifestyle is not looking better in six months. (That is the free and added bonus) We know that it feels bad to be living physically out of control. We must also realize that the flip side of that is that it also feels good to be physically living the way that we should.

Isn't it interesting that some people can get addicted to fitness? Fitness contains enough instant intrinsic reward to become motivating or even addicting for some people. Fitness is interesting. View it one way and we procrastinate and avoid it. View it another and we can get so much intrinsic reward from it that some people get addicted and never want to stop. That instant intrinsic reward is there. We must get into the mindset to expect and get that payoff.

We are not all getting the same emotional payoff for fitness. Rather, we are chemically getting the experience we expect ourselves to have.

The fix for the motivational nightmare many of face when it comes to our emotional goal lies in finding and experiencing that instant reward. When we get into the mindset to expect and experience and appreciate the instant reward of fitness and eating the way we should, we don't' have to motivate ourselves to do them.

> When we get INSTANT REWARD in the form of feeling good about ourselves or getting energy, pride, and positive emotion when we eat right and workout the way we should, those things become INTRINSICALLY MOTIVATING of their own accord.

Feeling good about skipping that cake can feel even better than eating it if you let it. it is mindset and getting intentional about letting yourself feel that INSTANT REWARD of doing the right things that will make them so much easier for us to do.

When fitness and eating right themselves give us a powerful instant reward in the form of a shot of pride, a sense of control and the flood of positive emotion, those things get instantly rewarded in our heads.

Instant reward is incredibly motivating. Recognizing THE POWER OF INSTANT REWARD by a business makes some people very rich. Recognizing the power of INSTANT REWARD as a tool for your own motivation can radically change your drive to do the things you do.

Motivationally, instant reward is the difference between hating your job and struggling through two weeks to reach that paycheck and getting paid to do the things you love and really want to do anyway.

That weight loss you want is the paycheck. Your love of the job is the way you feel on the track it takes to get there.

There is no longer any need to choose the road you hate now for the payoff you want with your body later one. That is a motivational nightmare. When that ultimate payoff is also in line with the rewards of a process you love along the way, there is no conflict between now and the future that makes it so hard.

Motivationally, like everything else. the difference is found in a mindset. Learn to love and reward that things that have the power to love you back and get you where you want to be in the end!

Give yourself that instant emotional payoff for doing the things that you do. That instant emotional payoff is FAR more motivating than that cake. There is no need to struggle for six long months through something we dislike for that ultimate payoff. Motivationally, that is just too hard, and we are likely not going to last. Luckily, reframing and seeing it differently will give you that instant emotional and energy payoff that you will feel immediately.

There is plenty of intrinsic, instant reward and that, along with the intentional emotional reward you purposefully give yourself are more than enough instant gratification to make it feel good to walk past that cake, do that workout or eat that salad for your lunch!

Reward the right things in yourself and you will get the right behavior. Motivationally, there is nothing more powerful than the draw of feeling good right now, so reward the good thing you do by letting yourself feel good the moment you do them!

IT FEEL REALLY GOOD TO BE ON TRACK

You know how bad to feels to be off track? Of course, you do. It kills you personally with the hit to your energy and self-esteem.

For all of us it feels physically and emotionally bad to be off track in our physical lives. It mentally and physically hurts when we are. The flip side of that is true as well. It FEELS REALLY GOOD to be on track toward our physical goals. It feels just as good to be going the right direction ad be back in charge of ourselves and our lives physically. One reason to get back on track physically is it gets rid of that pain and it feels really good!

We get hundreds of powerful instant payoffs for the things that we do right with our bodies. WE JUST HAVE TO RECOGNIZE IT AND LET OURSELVES HAVE THEM.

It feels good to get back on track. It feels good physically from day one if we see it in the right way.

Emotionally, we will never feel happier or stronger than when we also taking care of our bodies the way that we should.

We think the reward of fitness or eating right is months down the road, Really, the reward doesn't have to be saved for the end, and it shouldn't be. When you are in the right Body Mindset, you are going to feel good about doing the right things, right now.

We shouldn't see it as a sacrifice now that we do for the future. That's a motivational nightmare to maintain. Instead, we need to let ourselves be happier than ever before when we are on track and in the middle of the process it takes to get the body results that we want in the end. Don't save the reward for the end. Give it to yourself liberally DURING the process!

Motivationally, recognizing the power INSTANT EMOTIONAL REWARD, can change the entire motivational climate of the long game we play for the things we want in the end. Like all of life, the joy must be in the journey, and that journey must be in the direction of where you ultimately want to end up.

We used to think of our body goals as exchanging what we want at the moment for something we want more in the future.

That works, but it is old motivational science Maturity is not just holding out and bypassing the joy of an instant reward with something more important and bigger in the future. You can't just work for the money anymore. You need to learn to enjoy your job! Changing your motivation so that you get an instant reward now out of something that what you want now is in line with what you want later, and you get an instant reward out of now, is the best motivational science.

Change the way you see things that line up with your long-term goals so that you get an instant reward out of doing them now, and you will change the motivational game of doing them. Instant reward is not bad. Instead, is perhaps the most natural and powerful human motivator there is. We all want what we want now to be happy. We just have to learn to give it ourselves in ways that will encourage us toward that long term win we want in the end as well.

That motivational strategy of the future is a view of things that creates no conflict between what you want now and later. Luckily, old maturity was replaced by a mindset that makes it all WIN-WIN.

LEARN TO LOVE THE JOURNEY it takes to get the body you want, and you give yourself loads of instant emotional reward for doing the things it takes to get there. (You can't give yourself too much emotional reward for the right things, because you get more of the behavior you reward.)

Change the motivational climate of the things you do for your health and you will quit struggling to get yourself to do them. You can love your job AND love the money. Some of us are lucky enough to find or to build that into our lives with mindset.

You can also LOVE THE PROCESS of being on track and love the body you get by doing it. it is no longer necessary to choose what you want more a reward now or in the future. Just reward yourself will all the positive emotion you can feel and recognize all the POWERFUL REWARD you get instantly as soon as you work out or eat the way you should. INSTANT REWARD is instinct in the process of healthy living. You just need to recognize and expect it to feel it.

The more positive emotion you Reward yourself

With when you pass something you shouldn't have,

Or you have a good solid day with your body goals

Of you work out the way you planned,

The stronger and more on track you feel.

The more you reinforce and encourage good body
behavior

By letting yourself feel positive emotion when you do

The more good-body-behavior you will bring out in
yourself!

Reward good behavior with positive emotion and

You will get more good behavior out of yourself if you reward the right things that you do! Feeling good about the right things in your life when you them is powerful behavior modification.

REWARD GOOD BEHAVIOR WITH EMOTION

NEVER UNDERESTIMATE THE POWER OF USING EMOTION AS A REWARD FOR GOING IN THE RIGHT DIRECTION OR DOING THE RIGHT THINGS. Intentionally let yourself feel good about doing the right things and you will. One way to ensure you get on track and stay there is to instantly reward any progress you make with as must positive emotion, attention, and pride as you can give yourself. Behaviorally, we get more of what we focus on. Focus on the negative things that you do, and you get more negative. Focus on and the stuff you get right and let yourself feel proud and good about yourself for doing it and you will more confidently and powerfully move in the right direction. Focus on what you do wrong, and you will get more of that from yourself as well.

CELEBRATION BUILDS SUCCESS

> *When you celebrate success emotionally, you give yourself a huge boost in the momentum that you need to succeed.*

Emotionally, a huge part of building that cycle of success is the celebration, which elevates your mood and reinforces your behavior. Get the celebration right and you set the motivational tone of your journey. When you do something right, celebrate the heck out of it. Reward yourself with all the positive emotion and praise you can. When you are down, be a cheerleader. From this point forward, realize that there are consequences to the way you talk to, and treat yourself. Feeling good about yourself and your direction, gives you power. Feeling bad about it, takes that away. Emotionally celebrate EVERY step you take in the right direction and let yourself feel really good about it inside when you do. Equally, don't beat yourself up emotionally or let yourself feel bad when you do something wrong. You must create the emotionally support and mental environment that will make you feel good about you and be effective at the things that you do. Forgive, support, and encourage yourself to do better when you don't, make healthy food and a fit, and active level part of your life and your identity, and you will get to and live at a weight you want for the rest of your life Get the mental part of it right, and you will get the physical part as well.

SUMMARY OF

INSTANT EMOTIONAL REWARD

ONE WAY to ensure you get on track and stay there is to instantly reward any progress you make with as must positive emotion, attention, and pride as you can give yourself. From behavior experts, we know that behaviorally, we get more whatever we focus on. Well, that is true of what we focus on in ourselves as well. Focus on the negative things that you do, and you get more negative. Focus on and the stuff you get right and let yourself feel proud and good about yourself for doing it and you will more confidently and powerfully move in the right direction. Focus on what you do wrong, and you will get more of that from yourself as well.

CELEBRATE BABY STEPS

To change your direction, celebrate even the smallest steps you take in a new direction., Mentally celebrate and reward every step you take that is doing something right, no matter how small. If it is an improvement, reward and really let yourself feel good about doing it. The more you celebrate the positives, the more positives you will get from yourself.

Use positive reinforcement at every single step of this journey you take toward getting where you want to be, like you just hit a golden buzzer.

You can never reinforce a positive step you take too much!

DO NOT ALLOW YOURSELF TO DWELL ON ANY NEGATIVES. Motivationally and behaviorally, you will manifest what you focus on. Schedule your retreat and then celebrate that you made a time and a place in your life for this goal to begin. Celebrate that you

WE BEAT OURSELVES UP SO BADLY OVER BODY THINGS, WHICH OFTEN GETS US IN A BAD MENTAL PLACE, AND TELLS US WE ARE GOING IN THE

WHETHER IT IS FINDING JOY IN YOUR JOB, YOUR LIFE OR THE EATING AND WORKING THAT WILL HELP YOU ACCOMPLISH YOUR LONG-TERM GOAL, LEARNING HOW TO EMOTIONALLY WIN NOW AND IN THE FUTURE AND NOT LET THOSE TWO THINGS CONFLICT IS THE KEY TO REAL HAPPINESS AND MOTIVATION

The Body Mindset

did something to create change in your life. Celebrate that you are taking the time to get your head in the place.

CELEBRATION BUILDS ESTEEM

When you celebrate success emotionally, you give yourself a huge boost in the momentum that you need to succeed. When you celebrate what you get right, you build the esteem, efficacy, and momentum you need to go in the right direction.

Emotionally, a huge part of building that cycle of success is the celebration, which elevates your mood and reinforces your behavior. Get the celebration right and you set the motivational tone of your journey. When you do something right, celebrate the heck out of it.

Reward yourself with all the positive emotion and praise you can. When you are down, be a cheerleader. From this point forward, realize that there are consequences to the way you talk to, and treat yourself. Feeling good about yourself and your direction, gives you power. Feeling bad about it, takes that away.

Emotionally celebrate EVERY step you take in the right direction and let yourself feel really good about it inside when you do. Equally, don't beat yourself up emotionally or let yourself feel bad when you do something wrong.

You must create the emotionally support and mental environment that will make you feel good about you and be effective at the things that you do.

Forgive, support, and encourage yourself to do better when you don't, make healthy food and a fit, and active level part of your life and your identity, and you will get to and live at a weight you want for the rest of your life .

Get the mental part of it right,

and you will get the physical part as well.

CELEBRATE THE PROGRESS

To improve your motivation, you can never celebrate too much! Mentally celebrate and reward every step you take in the right direction. The more you celebrate the positives, the more positives you will get from yourself.

Use positive reinforcement at every single step of this journey you take toward getting where you want to be, like you just hit a golden buzzer.

You can never reinforce a positive step you take too much!

SCHEDULE YOUR RETREAT AND THEN CELEBRATE THAT YOU MADE A TIME AND A PLACE IN YOUR LIFE FOR THIS GOAL TO BEGIN. CELEBRATE THAT YOU DID

WE BEAT OURSELVES UP SO BADLY OVER BODY THINGS, WHICH OFTEN GETS US IN A BAD MENTAL PLACE, AND TELLS US WE ARE GOING IN THE WRONG DIRECTION. WHEN IT COMES TO OUR BODIES, WE OFTEN DO EVERYTHING WRONG MENTALLY!

WE BEAT OURSELVES UP MENTALLY OVER THE THINGS WE DO PHYSICALLY. WE DWELL ON EVERYTHING WE DO WRONG. WE ARE MENTALLY ROUGH ON OURSELVES IN WAYS THAT ARE JUST NOT NICE OR PHYSICALLY EFFECTIVE .INSTEAD, WE NEED TO REINFORCE AND CELEBRATE EVERY MOVE WE MAKE IN THE RIGHT DIRECTION

SOMETHING TO CREATE CHANGE IN YOUR LIFE. CELEBRATE THAT YOU ARE TAKING THE TIME TO GET YOUR HEAD IN THE PLACE.

CELEBRATE
EVERY STEP YOU TAKE
IN THE RIGHT DIRECTION

LEARN TO INSTANTLY AND EMOTIONALLY
CELEBRATE AND FEEL GOOD ABOUT WHAT
YOU DO RIGHT AND YOU WILL REINFORCE
THE RIGHT BEHAVIOR IN YOURSELF

LEARN FROM AND LET GO OF THE THINGS
YOU DO WRONG AND YOU WON'T REINFORCE
BAD BEHAVIOR OR MENTALLY GET ROLLING
IN THE WRONG DIRECTION IN YOUR LIFE.

FOCUS ON AND REWARD THE RIGHT THINGS
YOU DO, AND LEARN FROM AND DON'T LET
THE BAD ONES DEFINE YOU AND YOU WILL
SHAPE YOUR BEHAVIOR SO YOU CAN
RELIABLY GO IN THE RIGHT
DIRECTION.

The Body Mindset

CHAPTER

SEVEN

DISTRACTION AND PROCRASTINATION

Distraction is often a major deterrent to our body goals.

Achieving a goal requires us to avoid the distractions that causes us to squirrel off track after something else.

Keeping focus on your goal and not getting sidetracked or distracted off that path it takes to get there is essential if we are going to stay on track and make progress toward our body goals.

To turn things around physically, we must avoid the distraction that will pull us off course and keep

To achieve our goals, we must learn to keep our head in the game and our eyes on the prize until we

our focus and priority on our goal until we do.

To achieve our goals, we must quit getting distracted by our struggles AND by the chocolate cake we have in the kitchen.

Staying on track requires keeping our heads out of our distractors and excuses. It involves playing the long game by staying solidly on the right track until we get there. To do that, we must keep our minds and eyes off the things that could distract us away from our focus on that goal .

DISTRACTION AS A TOOL

We often think of distraction and procrastination as the enemies of our body goals. However, used right way, distraction and procrastination are powerful tools that will change the game and help you so you can achieve your body goals.

Besides often pulling off course, distraction is a powerful behavior modification tool as well. Distraction and procrastination are often necessary if we want to stay on course and achieve the goals we have set for our bodies and our lives.

Yes, distraction can be the enemy of your body goals, it can also be one the most powerful tools in your arsenal to help you accomplish them.

Distraction is the enemy of our body goals when it distracts us from them, but when you distract yourself from your thought of food, and , distraction used a different way, it can be the savior of them as well.

STAYING ON COURSE

The key to achieving our goals is to stay on course toward them over the long haul. Body goals are never short-term accomplishments. They require focus and staying on track for an extended amount of time.

We have good intentions. We plan. We start down the right path and distraction kills it. We get started on a track that will get us there, then we get distracted by life or problems or a pursuit that takes our focus away from our goal. We start well. We just can't stay on that path consistently enough to make real change because we get distracted.

Keeping our focus on progress and off thinking about our problems or the things we want on the side of that road, is necessary for the consistency it take to get real change.

Distraction is a major problem in our body goals. Achieving our body goals requires determination and consistency over time. We must avoid the distraction that will pull us off course.

If we want to go in a different place with our bodies physically, we must get consistent, and this means we must avoid will if we are going to get somewhere different with ourselves physically.

Learning to keep our eyes solitarily on a goal and avoid all the things that compete for our bandwidth and attention is essential to staying on track with the things that we do.

We must keep our focus on our goals and off the other things that are going on in our lives and our heads.

For some of us, the problem is not starting. It is staying on course. We start down the right path and get distracted by our cravings, our problem, our habits and all the other things on our minds that start competing for a piece of that. In short, we can't make any real and significant progress toward our body goals because we get distracted.

Achieving a goal in our lives, requires that we keep our eye on the prize and not get distracted by something else in our lives, thoughts, or emotions. We must keep thoughts on the right things and our eyes on priority on our goals if we are ever going to get there.

Success requires a singularity of focus. To achieve that goal, we must maintain our drive, our focus, and our positive direction.

No matter what you are trying to accomplish, there will be a hundred things out there that can distract your away from it.

Our lives and minds are so full that we must intentionally avoid the thoughts and distractors that that could entice and excuse us off the path that will get us there. Making that goal a real priority that we intend to accomplish at all cost and keeping our focus and priority on that task is a big part of being effective and achieving our goals.

USED CORRECTLY, DISTRACTION CAN BE A POWERFUL TOOL TO HELP YOU MAINTAIN YOUR WEIGHT AND ACHIEVE YOUR BODY GOALS.

TO ACHIEVE OUR GOALS, you must keep the big things front and center in our minds. Success of every kind requires we keep our eyes on the prize and avoid getting distracted off course.

With our body goals, the biggest distractors that pull us off course are:

WE HAVEN'T GOT THE RIGHT PRIORITY
We have so must we need and want to do that, with so many balls in the air, we can't keep our eyes or our focus on any of

them. Priority narrows down our focus so we can do the right things well.

LIFE GETS IN THE WAY.

Besides the trivial, distractions, most of us have very real-life problems that get in our way. Not only do we have to avoid getting distracted by the cheesecake, but we must also keep our focus on track through the very real problems and challenges of our lives.

Maintaining focus and priority through the trivial and major distractors of our lives is an essential part of successfully accomplishing our body goals.

We often see distraction as the enemy of all our body goals. However, used correctly is can district us from the wrong things as help us stay on track toward our body goals.

DISTRACTING YOURSELF FROM THAT PIZZA OR THIS CRAVING CAN HELP YOU STAY ON TRACK AND ACHIEVE YOUR BODY GOALS.

DISTRACTION USED CORRECTLY CAN GET YOUR MIND OFF THE WRONG THINGS AND KEEP YOU ON TRACK!

Distraction is bad when it cloudys up our emotional sky and distracts us from our goals. It is bad when we get distracted away from our goals and priorities, BUT distraction can also be a powerful way to manage our impulses and stay on track toward our goals as well. Sometimes we have to use distraction to get our mind off the things that will pull us off track.

Distraction is bad when it distracts us from good things. However, distraction is a powerfully and good behavior modifier when we distract ourselves from the things we shouldn't think of or do.

STAYING ON TRACK with our body goals often requires us to keep our minds off the wrong things. If you keep thinking about that candy, you're eventually going to eat it. if you keep thinking that emotionally negative thought, you will kill your emotion, and struggle with impulse control and the drive for emotional eating as well.

Distracting ourselves from that candy bowl involves getting it out of sight AND getting our minds off of it. Getting that negative thought out of our minds involves filling our mind and our hands with something else we really like to do. There are many times in life when distraction is our friend. When we distract ourselves from thoughts and impulses we shouldn't have, we stay on the track to where we really want to be.

Let's face it, we face multiple impulses to leave that healthy path each day. The best tool to stay on track is to get our mind and eyes off those distractors as soon as we can.

We will eventually cave to a craving if we let the thoughts of it circle around in our heads. Get that food 1) out of sight, 2) out of possibility, and 3) off of your mind with distraction. Don't look at it. Don't think about it and don't let yourself be around it. Instead, get busy and wrapped up in something else. Don't let a craving stay in your thoughts or you head. Get away from it and distract yourself with thoughts and actions about something else.

To stay on track, we often NEED the tool of DISTRACTION!

The longer we look at and considering the alternative, the more likely we are going to fall to its enticement. Let yourself consider the option of sleeping in and you are likely to convince yourself to do it. Let yourself think about those brownies, and you are likely to eat them.

Get the things you shouldn't have out of sight, and then get them out of mind with the tool of distraction. Stay busy mentally and physically with something that takes both your head and your hands, and you won't have time to consider or think about the things that you crave.

Distract yourself from your cravings as well as the thoughts you shouldn't allow yourself to have. Sometimes, we just need to turn off our thinking, wrap our minds and bodies up in something else so we can stay on track.

Nike's slogan, "Just do it," implies that thought can also be our enemy. With our body goals we have the tendency to engage in that mental battle we have over doing them. We often need to distract ourselves away from all that thought or consideration when we do them. Turn off your thought about doing those things with distraction.

Don't allow that mental battle over whether or not you will. Instead distract yourselves away from thoughts of it being hard, things that you want instead and reason you think of for why you can't. Keep your head, hands and bodies distracted from the wrong thought about things. use distraction to take your head out of it when your head is the enemy. Turn off the wrong and obsessive thought you have with distraction so you can it routine to 'Just Do It' physically the way that you planned.

We naturally have a tendance to talk ourselves out of our goal and good intentions when we allow ourselves to argue or debate over it. Don't let yourself mentally suffer or struggle mentally with doing it. Instead, fill your heads with other thoughts and keep your hands and body busy so you won't.

Stay busy enough with the right things and you won't even entertain the thought of doing the wrong things. when you mind and hand and bodies are busy, you can't let your minds consider or debate going off track. Sometimes the best way to stay the course with your body goals is to keep your minds and hands too busy to do otherwise with distraction. To do this:

- Go on a run
- Pull weeds in the garden
- Pull out your paints
- Get into a lively conversation with someone
- Grow a business
- Get outside with your kids
- Put more mental and physical effort into your job
- Start a business
- Do a craft
- Connect with friends
- Fall in love
- Fill your mind with gratitude
- Find compassion
- Learn a skill
- Sing a song
- Make a plan.
- Turn up the music and dance

DISTRACT YOURSELF IN ALL THE RIGHT WAYS, AND YOU WON'T FOCUS ON OR OBSESS OVER THE THINGS THAT WILL TAKE YOU DOWN.

One way to stay on track with your body goal is to learn how to distract yourself in all the right ways. Keep your mind and hands and body busy in the right way and you won't even think about food until your body tells you to. Distraction can be bad, when you get distracted from the wrong things, but it can also be a powerful behavior modification strategy when you use it right.

Keep your mind and body busy with the right thoughts and the right things and the wrong things won't enticed you or get you obsessed with the thoughts that will pull you off course.

WE ALREADY USE DISTRACTION

Distraction gets a bad rap in our world. We need to recognize that we already know how to use distraction to modify behavior and we do it all the time. If you are a parent, you likely already know about and use the powerful tool of distraction to modify and gently change behavior.

As parents, we distract our kid from things they shouldn't think or do all the time. When our kids are misbehaving or feeling an overwhelming emotion, we distract and redirect them to something better or more positive they can think or do. We just need to do the same for ourselves.

Seamlessly, distraction can avoid the negativity of discipline or the drama of changing behavior in any other way. As parents, we become very good at distraction as a tool of behavior modification. We choose our battles and learning moments at times, and at others we simply use distraction to redirect our kids to away from things they shouldn't do, think, or feel.

Distraction is powerful tool we already know and use fluidly to manage behavior. We just need to use it for ourselves as well.

Distraction maintains the peace while keeping thing going in the right direction, as seamlessly, and positively as possible. By simply getting our mind's, or our children's minds on something else, we can **keep the peace**, keep **make things run smoothly**, and **avoid the emotional drama** it takes to get where we need to go without negativity or punishment. Distraction is a more powerful behavior modification strategy than we give it credit for.

By using distraction to also keep our body goals rolling along in the right direction without allowing ourselves to suffer over or sweat them we can also seamlessly keep things rolling along positively in the right direction with our goals and our bodies most of the time.

As parents, it is often best to simply distract our kids from their negative behavior and emotion by getting their minds involved in something else. NOT SURPRISINGLY, THAT IS ALSO OFTEN BEST FOR US!

THE ROLE OF DISTRACTION IN OUR BODY GOALS

IT IS THE IMPULSE TO DO OR THINK THE THINGS WE SHOULDN'T

THAT GENERALLY RUIN OUR EMOTION AND RESULTS.

The key to using the behavior control in ourselves is also to use the tool of distraction to reduce the drama of staying on track or the obsessing over things we shouldn't have. if there is not good reason to let your mind be where it is, whether it is on that chocolate cake or something that went wrong at work, then use distraction to get your hands, mind, and body into something else.

One of the best ways to stay on track is simply to distract yourself from thinking about or doing the things you shouldn't do. We think of distraction something that is bad for our body goals. However, Distraction can be a powerful tool that can dramatically change the game of emotion and success when distract ourselves from things that are bad.

THE ROLE OF DISTRACTION IN WILLPOWER

Perhaps you have heard that we only have a finite amount of willpower. When we battle an impulse all day, we use up the willpower that we have. The less we have to battle with or think about our options, the easier it will be to stay on track. Getting your mind, hand and eyes off the wrong things will significantly reduce the amount of willpower it takes to accomplish your body goals.

Instead of thinking about that cake, distract yourself with pulling those weeds in the garden. Let your mind squirrel away onto that book you are reading, or a project that will fill your mind, and your hands. Let your minds squirrel away from that cake and get involved in a task that will keep you on track toward your goal.

So, get out in the garden for a while. By the time, your back is in the sun and your mind and hands are busy pulling weeds, you will feel so good and be so busy, you will forget about the cake. Then, by the time you go back into the house, you will so good and proud of yourself for doing it, that the emotional boost you got from doing that will propel you right past that cake and into the things you should do. You likely won't even care about that cake by the time you come in.

Part of keeping our minds off temptation, of course is to not allow that cake in the house in the first place if you can avoid it. However, there will always be opportunities to go off track somewhere in our day. We can't physically avoid temptation forever. We are going to need to learn the tool of distraction to keep ourselves on track someday anyway.

Distraction works because our brains don't multitask very well. By filling our minds and hands with something else, they mentally drop the ball on the train of thought they shouldn't have.

To reduce the willpower requirement of this goal, learn to distract yourself from the thoughts and things enticing you to leave that path. To use distraction powerfully, get your mind off your cravings and out of that 'should I let myself out of this or not' battle you have with this goal in your head. Use distraction to help keep you on track by getting your mind and body:

- too busy
- Too messy
- Too involved
  And too happy to even think about food until your stomachs insists that you do. Get your mind off food by getting into the joy of life! Find your flow.

Get happy, get busy and get into something you care about and you will naturally get your mind off temptation and your head out of places it has no good reason to go. ONE OF THE BEST WAYS to keep yourselves peacefully and happily on track toward our body goals is to use the power of distraction to help you stay there.

IT DOESN'T HAVE TO TAKE THAT MUCH WILLPOWER

We think achieving our body goals takes superhuman amounts of willpower. It doesn't really take that much if you mentally do it right. Keep your mind out of places where you might find willpower battle. Keep foods you shouldn't have and struggle with out of your house. Make it convenient and refuse to allow the thoughts and willpower battles in your mind that make it hard to do.

It only takes a lot of willpower to avoid the things we let ourselves battling with doing in our heads. If we keep our minds in the right place, IT DOESN'T TAKE AS MUCH WILLPOWER to stay on track with our body goals as we thought.

Distraction helps distract you from that willpower battle, plus, you get bonus points for all the things you get done, and even more for the physical activity you get out of doing them. Distraction is a powerful goal that can take away the challenge of achieving your body goals.

THE POWER OF PROCRASTINATION

Procrastination is another negative that can be turned around to become a positive tool to help with our weight loss and our body goals.

The Power of Procrastination is that when we put off our cravings and sometimes even our hunger, they often just go away on their own.

Procrastination is remarkably like distraction, except that instead of distracting ourselves from something forever, we procrastinate that impulse to space our eating out so we can achieve our body goal. Procrastination doesn't 't mean we will never again eat sugar. It doesn't mean we and never again have something we like. It does mean that we need to quit giving in to our instant impulses and procrastinating the impulses we have to eat something the minute we think about doing it.

We often get distracted off course by our hunger, cravings, inability to stabilize our own emotions. Sometimes the best way to get past a craving is to drink some water and procrastinate satisfying that craving long enough that it goes by itself.

THE TWENTY MINUTE RULE

Surprisingly, most cravings end within twenty minutes whether we give into them or not. In fact, ignoring and procrastinating that craving is often the best way to avoid the next one.

Often, eating that food we crave, just makes us crave more, or reduces our ability to say no to the next thing. Many of us incorrectly believe that the only way to get rid of a craving is to feed it.

Really, most cravings will go away completely if we just put them off for twenty minutes.

We think the way to get rid of cravings is to feed them, however, feeding a craving, often just makes it worse. Food companies know that the taste of a food often triggers the impulse to eat it. That's why they give free samples. Instead of feeding a craving, try drink a tall glass of water, looking at the clock and making yourself wait 20 minutes before you think about that food again.

Surprisingly, even the pangs of real hunger often go away or gets easier to manage if you wait 20 minutes. (Good to know for times you are trying to make it to bedtime without ruining your diet, times you can't eat for medical reasons or times you have chosen intermittent fasting as a solution.)

> *You gain a lot of power over your hunger and cravings if you learn the rule of 20, which is that if you drink some water and wait, most cravings an often even real hunger will go away for a while if procrastinate that impulse for about 20 minutes and those feelings pass.*

A STONECUTTER HAMMERS AWAY AT A ROCK HUNDREDS OF TIMES

UNTIL SUDDENLY, ON THE FINAL HIT IT SPLITS IN TWO.   – JACOB RUIZ

Don't think what you are doing is not working It doesn't always show on the scale or your body until the day that it does.

PERSISTENCE

With enough persistence and determination, you will get where you want to go. Persistence and determination in life are far more important than talent or where you are when you begin. If you get determined enough and refuse to give up, you will change the process and learn from your mistakes as you go until you get where you want to be.

NO MATTER HOW MANY TIMES YOU

FALL DOWN IN YOUR GOAL

GET UP AND LEARN WHAT

YOU CAN FROM THAT FALL

YOU WILL ACCOMPLISH

YOU GOAL IF YOU REMEMBER

ONE THING

Baby Ruth told us,

"You just can't beat the person who never quits".

Every strike out brings you closer to the next home run.

CHAPTER
EIGHT

FOOD AND ENERGY

We often reach for food when we feel a dip in our energy, or our motivation or our emotion is low. One thing that really hurts our body goals is not understanding the connection between food and the energy we feel.

When we feel a dip in our energy we reach for food, believing it is food we need to give us energy. Actually, that is not the way it works. In fact, our drive and energy are often highest when our bodies biologically have the need for food.

We reach for food because we misunderstand the kind of energy, we get from eating. Yes, we get energy from food, but not the kind of energy we think we will. From food, we get cellular energy. We get the building blocks of life, not always the feeling of motivation and energy that we want. Instead, like a well-fed lion, our energy and motivation are often at its lowest when our body has been well fed.

Biologically, it makes sense that hunger keeps us on top of our game. Biologically, we must be our sharpest and most alert when our bodies need food. Nature ensures that we are at the top of our game when we are hungry, so we have the energy to pursue our food and the mental sharpness to outsmart it.

We eat for that boost of energy we think we are going get from food, only to feel a dip in our mood and our energy when we do. Then feeling groggy and sorely disappointed, we often just eat more, hoping that this time it will work.

Sometimes we overeat because we think that will give us the boost of energy and motivation that we need.

The term 'hungry salesman' also comes from the fact that when our need is high, so is our energy and motivation. A hungry salesman, like a hungry lion must be 'on point,' motivated, and on top of their game, while I well fed lion or a salesman who has lost that drive is too satisfied to be on top his game.

Eating lightly and staying just a little less than 'satisfied' gives us more energy and drive in a day than we have when we eat to our complete satisfaction. We will have more energy and sharpness in life when eat to keep ourselves just a little bit hungry.

Our problem with food is sometimes just with vocabulary. We want the kind of energy we feel. We want an experience. We get the energy out bodies need to sustain life and repair themselves so they can live. We reach for food thinking we are going to get the kind of energy we want. Instead, we get a mental fog and the feeling that we physically need a nap because our bodies want to do it lie down, take a nap and digest.

Instead of giving us the that buzz we want, eating the wrong foods or the wrong amount of food often zaps our energy. Then, thinking it's not working, we reach for another cookie or eat something else. Some of the overeating we do is a misunderstanding we have with the kind of energy our bodies receive from food. We want the motivation for the hunt. Our bodies get the motivation to take a nap and digest. Sometimes we overeat because we don't understand the relationship between hunger, energy, and motivation the way it exists in nature.

Food keeps the lights on. It gives us cellular energy. It doesn't give us the motivation to finish our day that we want. Food nourishes our cells, maintains our body temperature, and gives our cells the energy they need to perform their specialized tasks. Food give is the energy to keeps the lights on. It keeps us alive. It does not provide the motivational energy or boost in our afternoon energy dip the way we think it will.

We eat when we we're bored, when our mood is low or when what we really need is water or sleep. We eat when we feel a dip in motivation or energy. We eat to feel one thing. Instead, we get the impulse to lie down and digest the food we ate.

The second culprit to that dip in energy we feel about eating is our own disappointment and frustration with ourselves for doing it. when we fall down in our body goals or personal expectations, we often feel depressed or frustrated with ourselves for not doing what we thought we should. This frustration we feel after we eat that surgery donut or candy bar is another culprit that zaps our energy and makes us feel bad when we do.

Actually, eating light and healthy food, like vegetables and lean protein, will keeps us sharp and make us feel the best kind of motivational energy that we can. Don't fall for the belief that eating more will give you that kind of energy and you won't overeat in the effort to find it.

EVERY GREAT ACCOMPLISHMENT

OR CHANGE OF DIRECTION EVER

BEGIN WITH A DECISION

The Body Mindset

CHAPTER
NINE

A POWERFUL DECISION

"That day I made a clear decision. I was sick and tired of QUITTING! I was going to stick with it and show up imperfectly for myself."

By Shaelee Phillips

Like my mom mentioned earlier, I grew up with very tiny sisters and that messed with my head. I was the biggest of the 5 girls in my family and taller than most of the boys in class. At 16 I was taller and bigger than my boyfriend and I guess you could say I had a case of body dysmorphia for a lot of years.

If I had been more confident in my skin at the time, it wouldn't have bothered me, but like most teenagers, I was SUPER insecure, and that followed me into my adulthood for a while. I was uncomfortable in my own skin and trying to figure out who I was and where I fit in. For years I was convinced I was big boned, awkward, clumsy and a dumb blonde. These thoughts paved the way for the choices I made as well.

My mom loves joking with me about being "too tired on Mondays" but it was true. It wasn't just tumbling class on Monday night though; it was soccer practice on Tuesdays and so on. I was NOT interested in difficult tasks and I was basically looking for the path of least resistance in my life. . If it was hard or didn't come naturally to me, I would give up.

Deep down, I knew I wanted to feel better and do better, but I didn't know how to get there. I wanted to look good and I could not figure it out. Part of me knew what I needed to do, but the other part wanted to find an easier way.

I knew I needed to move 30 minutes a day.

I knew I needed to drink more water.

I knew I needed to eat more vegetables.

I knew what I needed to do, but I honestly didn't want to put in the work. It all sounds easy when you say it, and it is when you get going, but it wasn't easy for me, at first. It wasn't until I got my mind in the right place that I was able to get abs for the first time in my life, and I did it AFTER having 3 kids.

Don't get me wrong, abs are nice and all, but my favorite gains by far are internal.

I agree with my mom. There is a mental headspace that is hard to explain. When you step out of your old way mentally it takes you to new levels you never thought possible. Now I am obsessed with pushing my personal limits and helping others break their own glass ceilings. When you do what feels difficult or impossible in your mind, you gain so much confidence and strength that it transfers to other areas of your life as well.

Once you know WHAT you want and WHY you want it, it's time to commit to go after it. There is so much power in making a CLEAR and CONSCIOUS decision and taking immediate ACTION toward that goal. For me it all started with a commitment to myself to STOP QUITTING. I simply committed to being the best version of ME and, this time, I made the decision to do it from a place of love rather than a place of hate and disgust with myself.

I HIT MY OWN PERSONAL LOW

All my physical improvement started 6 years ago after I had my 2nd daughter Hayzlee. At that time, I hit some postpartum depression and started taking it out on my husband. Today, I keep those letters I wrote to him at the time to remind myself how far I've come.

I was angry at my husband, Bray for not giving me the love and attention I needed to feel better. Inside, I was bitter for not being able to do better with things by myself. As a new mom naturally I gave everything to my baby, but in doing that, I had nothing left for myself.

I couldn't remember who Shaelee even was anymore and because of that, I was starving for validation and affection from others. When I didn't get what I thought I needed, it tore me up. I had no idea that what I needed and craved more than anything else was love and acceptance from myself. I was looking outside for a happiness that I needed to give myself on the inside.

Having my second child mentally and physically slapped me in the face. I made a decision that would change that with my third. (I will go into more detail about it in my next book *The Baby Body Mindset)* but let's just say I hit my rock bottom after my second daughter was born. I hated the way I looked. I felt powerless and needy and I was depressed, angry, and sad all at the same time. I hit a personal and physical low.

Then one day in June of 2015, I walked into a local aerial fitness studio. There were girls doing silks, hammock, lyra (the hoop), and pole fitness. I tried not to stare at how strong and flexible these women and men were. I wondered "how can someone move that way?" They were all strong, flexible, graceful, confident, and in my eyes, they were fearless.

I could barely lift my feet an inch off the ground that day. I felt like an awkward baby duckling. I was frustrated, jealous, and discouraged and I wondered "why am I not good at anything?"

I didn't know I would get where I am today, but that day I made a clear decision. I was sick and tired of QUITTING things and I was going to stick with this. I just decided to quit quitting!

I decided to show up for myself imperfectly from where I was. I decided to stop comparing myself with others, grow where I was planted, and only compete with the person in the mirror. I was done letting my excuses win. I wanted to see what would happen if I stuck with something longer than one year.

Flash forward 6 years and I've been coaching others online and at home or 4 years now and I loving it. I'm doing pole fitness performances for others. I just started training with acrobatic yoga. I do trapeze with my husband. :) Last week I ran a 10-mile relay untrained and had no problems with it, and I just hit a front hand spring for the first time by myself.

I am in the best shape of my life at 30 years old. I can't believe I'm getting better and even learning new flips at my age.

I surprise myself daily and so will YOU!

And it all starts with just one decision.

THE POWER OF A TRULY COMMITTED DECISION

Both Shaelee and I had to make powerful decisions to change our bodies. We both had to make powerful, not going back decisions to do it in our lives. Shaelee's words of power were, "I'm done quitting things in my life." Mine were, "I don't care if it kills me, I'm done going in that direction physically in my life."

Change is hard. When we first change our bodies, the inertia of our normal eating and physical routine pulls at us to stay there. At first, a change in our eating or activity it doesn't feel natural or comfortable because it is not the path we've been on or what we are used to. Our bodies struggle to maintain homeostasis, the steady internal, physical and chemical conditions that living systems naturally maintain. We have to use the power of our minds and commitment of our decisions to stay on a track that feel unfamiliar and sometimes uncomfortable at first, until we reach a new level of homeostasis.

In short, we must use the power of our minds and the commitment of our decision to do what doesn't feel natural or comfortable at first until we get settle into that new track.

Those of us who are quite overweight, like I was, feel the change in the way we eat and move dramatically at first. It takes a decision made with the right level of mental commitment to overcome the inertia of the path we have been on and keeps us on track until it becomes our new norm and gets easier to do.

We return to a track that feels familiar, even when that path is not making us happy or getting us where we want to be. Our struggle to stay consistent is there and we won't do it, unless we make a decision with the power it takes to get us on a new track. Think of a powerful decision as the rocket that will boost you to a new and different orbit.

POWERFUL DECISIONS

Not all of the decisions we make to change our bodies or our lives are created equal. The kind of decision you make to do something in your mind is the difference between doing it and falling apart and excusing yourself out of it when things get hard.

Only the decisions we make with the right kind of power in our minds are capable of getting us where we want to be.

we choose to go the moon...not because it is easy but because it is a challenge we are willing to accept.

When I think of powerful decisions, I often think of the one that JFK made that committed America to go to the moon.

When JFK spoke to the American people on that historic day in 1962, he did so with the complete commitment to a vision. He spoke with an unwavering conviction that we were going to achieve a goal, even though, at present he had any idea how we were going to do it. He committed fully to a result and whatever it would take to get there.

In his speech, John F. Kennedy shared his vision and that decision with the American people. The people quickly get behind his plan and committed to that goal as well. From the taxpayers who funded it, to the engineers and scientists who designed it, to the astronauts that vigorously trained and were willing to risk their lives to do it, JFK fired up a nation who committed fully to a simply audacious goal.

In that speech, JFK proclaimed:

> **"We choose to go to the moon in this decade and do the other things, *not because they are easy, but because they are hard*, because this goal will serve to organize and measure the best of our energies and skills, because <u>this challenge is one that we are willing to accept, one we are unwilling to postpone, and one which we intend to win</u>."**

Are you ready to make that kind of a commitment in your mind to lose the weight, or get fit, or get yourself on a different physical track than the ones you've been on?

That is the kind of mental commitment that makes ALL of our lofty and audacious goals become possible. If, like me, you are a couch potato with a hundred pounds to lose, or like Shaelee, you need to find the power to become enough in your head and quit quitting at your own body goal, then you need a decision with the power to organize an sustain the effort it takes to do it.

FAR TOO MANY OF OUR BODY GOALS ARE DOOMED
FROM THE MOMENT WE MAKE THEM BECAUSE
WE NEVER FULLY COMMIT TO DO THEM.

The right kind of decision will bring out skill, ability and resilience you didn't even know you had. For many of us, committing to stay the course physically is committing to get to the moon. It is a big, scary, audacious goal, but then again, like JFK told us, we need a goal that is big enough *not because it is easy, but because it is hard enough to* **organize and measure the best of our energies and skills**.

Don't be afraid of committing to the big, audacious goal that scares you a little bit to do it. You need that level of goal and that kind of mental commitment to something to organize your focus and bring out the best of your energy and your skills. It may be scary to close those f exits of failure you hold onto in this goal and commit to staying the course and doing this until you do, but often, like it was for both of us, a commitment to a goal like that organizes your energy and fixes everything else.

We NEED our big, scary, audacious goals! They are the kite strings that hold us up and let us fly into the winds that blow us around us. When we turn our backs and run in fear from a challenge that is hard, we crash in our minds as well as with our goals. We need to do and get through things that are hard because, full commitment to the big, hard goals that scare us, brings out the best of us. We need it to be hard and to push through it to bring out the best of our energies and skills. When it gets hard, run into the wind, not away from it.

THE RIGHT KIND OF DECISION WILL GIVE

YOU THE POWER TO ACHIEVE YOUR GOAL

Not all the decisions we make to do something in life are created equal. Not all the decision we make to change our bodies or accomplish a goal are either. I made that decision to lose weight perhaps a hundred times, before I made 'THE DECISION' that gave me the power to do it.

The decision to change our bodies must come with the right kind of power and commitment in our minds. We must mentally close the BACK OUT PLANS in our minds.

The decision we make to do it, must leave no room for failure at all.
At first, I committed to 'try.'
I commit to do it 'unless it gets too hard.'
I committed 'as long as the problems in my life didn't get in the way.'

When I got into the mindset it took to do it, for the first time in my life, I committed to a body goal and made a decision to it that I "FULLY INTENDED to win."

When I mentally closed my exits and made that a NO EXCUSES, NO FAILURE, policy for myself in my head. I quit failing. I had to make a decision with the commit it took to fire myself up and get through the hard. Until I made that level of full committed to do it in my own head, I would go off course when my mood, my power or my mental or physical energy was low. Lets face it, until I get fully, mentally on board, I would go off track just because someone randomly brought donuts or pizza to work!

.

I had to commit to my own decision to do this with all my heart. I had to make it my personal priority to get this done.

My goal had to be bigger to me than eating cake at every birthday/family party or excusing myself from exercise on the days I didn't feel like it. I had to get fully, mentally into the point that it no longer had to be easy or to fit my life or mood as a prerequisite.
I had to get fired up and fully commit to doing this in my mind before I could find the power inside myself to get it done.

SET YOUR MIND ON THIS GOAL
When I was young, my mom used to tell me I could do anything I set my mind on doing. I didn't' understand what it means to SET YOUR MIND on doing something with the right kind of power that day.

What mom never knew was to get effective with a body goal, you have set your mind to it with that same kind of power and determination that you do with anything else you want to effectively do.

Most of us have committed to a body goal, unsuccessful before. Like Shaelee mentioned above, she knew in that moment it was a decision unlike any other, and that was my experience too. We're all at different stages of our journey but that doesn't matter. The only person we need to compete with is ourselves. When we start getting clear, organizing our efforts, and take away the option to fail, we will buckle down and do it.

When you commit to a body goal
With the level of commitment
It takes to get it done, you
COMMIT TO A GOAL

THAT THIS TIME YOU FULLY INTEND TO WIN.

Making a decision with the power and commitment it takes to get it done is the difference between a successful body makeover and one that is not.

Every person who has an impressive makeover story had a point where they mentally committed to that decision with the power it takes to get it done. The only things standing between you and the impressive makeover story of your life, is a clear decision and taking action.

Are you ready to commit:

NOT BECAUSE IT IS EASY
BUT BECAUSE DOING THIS
HARD THING WILL BRING OUT THE
BEST OF YOUR ENERGIES AND SKILLS?

ARE YOU READY TO TAKE ON A REAL CHALLENGE?
WITH THE COMMITMENT IT WILL TAKE
TO SEE IT THROUGH?

ARE YOU WILLING TO ACCEPT
THIS CHALLENGE FULLY INTO YOUR LIFE?
ARE YOU UNWILLING TO POSTPONE

IT ANY LONGER?
ARE YOU READY TO MAKE A
NEW KIND OF COMMITMENT
TO ACCOMPLISH THE BODY GOAL,

ARE YOU READY TO MAKE A DECISION TO DO THIS
THAT IS POWERFUL ENOUGH TO GET IT DONE?

Your true power only becomes apparent
after you reach the tipping point
of priority and determination
it takes to get it done.

MAKE A DECISION POWERFULLY
ENOUGH TO GET THIS DONE.

- Makes it a true priority to you in your mind.
- Takes away **failure as an option you can choose**.
- Makes you **quit caring if it is going to be hard.**

The right kind of decision to accomplish your body goal will make it a true personal priority for you, get you fully determined to do it and help you find **power, strength, and ability you didn't even know you had**

Once something becomes a Hell, or Highwater priority in a decision you make, you will find the kind of power and ability it takes to get it done.

YOUR REAL POWER AND ABILITY
WON'T EVEN SHOW UP UNTIL YOU REACH THE LEVEL
OF PRIORITY AND DETERMINATION, IT TAKES TO MAKE IT HAPPEN

You can lose 100 lbs. or 30 or 10. You can achieve a goal of visible abs. You can run a marathon. You can accomplish almost any goal in your life, if you make the kind of committed decision it will take to do it.

Only you can soul search that out and reach that point inside yourself. Only you can make a decision THAT YOU FULLY INTEND TO WIN in your heart. When you wrap your head around your own willingness to commit to this and you fire yourself up with the goal in your mind, that decision you made to do it won't be at all the same as one you have made in the past. You will fire yourself us with the grit and stamina it will take to get it done.

QUIT CONSIDERING THE ALTERNATIVE

Along with that commitment comes the decision to quit even letting yourself consider the alternative. When I used to encounter pizza, or I wanted to sleep in, I would turn to that part of my brain that wanted me to reconsider and say, "SORRY, THAT DECISION HAS ALREADY BEEN MADE.'"

You MUST quit considering the alternatives or you are likely to fail. You must turn off all that agonizing battle you have with your own willpower and say, I don't want to hear it. THIS DECISION HAS ALREADY BEEN MADE. If you engage in dialog with that Chubby Little Devil on your shoulder, he will persuade you with every reason he had that you should excuse yourself from your goal, 'just for today.' Mentally start listening to his reasons and you've already lost that battle in your head!

That side of your brain that wants you to fail is such a powerful persuader that if you ALLOW YOURSELF TO LISTEN to the reasons why you can't, you will lose the battle with your own resolve. With your kids, sometimes you simply have to say, no more. You are doing this because I said so and I won't listen to any more discussion about that. It's not that much different with your body. The part of you that is that is still a child inside wants to convince you with all the self-pity and powerful persuasion it has about why you can't do it today or you really deserve and need that cake.

Don't engage in that conversation with that part of yourself in your mind. Just say no. I'm not going to listen or consider the alternative. I already made this decision. We're doing this and I don't want to hear any more about it. Refuse to engage with that mental conversation with the part of you that wants you to fail. **Make a decision that is powerful enough to stay made and** *quit considering the alternative.*

- Close the exits on the road to success by refusing to even engage with that dialog tht makes you consider not following your plan.

To start a movement inside yourself making a powerful decision to go in a different direction from a place of clarity in your mind. Get fully committed to that plan and refuse to engage with the thoughts that try to temporarily excuse yourself away from following it. MAKE A ONE TIME DECISION to do this and then LET THAT DECISION STAY MADE!

IN CASE YOU FORGOT TO

REMIND YOURSELF THIS MORNING:

YOUR BUTT IS PERFECT!

YOUR SMILE LIGHTS UP THE ROOM!

YOUR MIND IS INSANELY COOL!

AND YOU ARE WAY

MORE THAN ENOUGH

STAY THE COURSE AND BELIEVE IN
YOURSELF BECAUSE, YOU ARE

WAY MORE AMAZING

THAN YOU KNOW!

CHAPTER

TEN

CHANGE YOUR RELATIONSHIP WITH FOOD AND FITNESS

by me, Shaelee K Phillips

Choosing healthy over skinny is choosing self-love over self-judgement.

~ Steve Maraboli.

CHANGE YOUR REASON

One of the best ways to change your relationship with food and fitness is to change the reason you do it. For years, I ate and worked out to be thin, and that was it. When I changed my objective and I chose to get strong and healthy instead of skinny, it changed everything. I began eating and working out in ways that were good for my body so I could build and take care of it. I quit neglecting and abusing it by alternating between excess and starvation like I used to when my goal was to be thin.

Diet Mindset vs. Healthy Lifestyle Mindset

My commitment to get strong and healthy came from my new commitment to self-love. I was no longer doing this because I hated my body, I was doing this because I loved my body.

For most of my life I viewed working out and "dieting" as a way to get skinny at that was it. I was so uncomfortable in the skin I was in, but I also dreaded working out and I failed at every diet I attempted. I couldn't seem to stick with anything long term and I always felt so much guilt when "I messed up." This would send me in a downward spiral of emotional eating. It was a constant and frustrating cycle... Sound familiar?

When you are eating or working out for health and strength, you eat and move differently than you did when the goal was to be thin. Your motivation feels different as well. When you make the shift from a diet mindset to a lifestyle mindset everything changes.

Nowadays I don't even like using the word "diet." To start, it has the word DIE in it also implies this is going to be a SHORT-TERM eating habit change.

The truth is, the key to a long term weight loss success is committing to a lifelong healthy lifestyle. This includes nutrient dense food choices and physical activity on a daily basis. There is no short cut or magic pill that will change your life. The secret is found in your daily routine.

So many of us have adopted this "immediate gratification, least amount of work" mindset and this is why FAD diets are so dang tempting. They promise fast results, but did you know 95% of people who go on diets gain their weight back?

I'm going to warn you now, this journey is not going to be easy, some days it's going to test you, but I promise YOU it will be worth it!!!

Self-love is not neglect or starvation. You can starve yourself thin, but you can't starve yourself healthy. You can maintain your weight reasonably by alternating between excess and starvation, but you won't have that healthy look or feel the way you wanted to.

One of the best reasons to have a healthy Body Mindset is self-love. When you decide to take care of your body and your mind in the best way possible, you have the motivation you need to begin to develop a long-term healthy relationship with food and fitness and healthy thoughts that will make you healthy and strong both inside and out. .

QUIT DANGLING DIVORCE

The second thing I had to do to get and stay on the right track, was to quit dangling divorce with that healthy lifestyle. I had to quit being ready to break up with my healthy eating or daily workout every time something went wrong.

I was not the type of person that would stick with things long-term if it wasn't easy or it didn't come naturally to me, I would quit. I just have to say that for most of my early life, commitment was not me.

When I was 7 years old, I remember my mom dropping me and my sister Brianna off for dance class every Monday night and she would often have a hard time getting me to get out of the car and go in. "I'm just tired on Mondays mom," I would tell her.

It took me years to become committed to daily fitness and healthy eating the way I am now. For years, I was always ready to quit as soon as something better came along, or things were going just right. Before I could ever get a better body, I had to get committed and quit dangling divorce with a healthy lifestyle.

EAT FOR THE RIGHT REASONS

. I used to eat for comfort. I ate to celebrate. I ate from boredom or even for bragging rights instead of eating for the real nutritional needs of my body.

To get control of my relationship with food I had to learn to listen to my body and eat for its needs instead of every other reason I had for consuming that food. To get control of my body I had to put food back in the real place of food and learn to eat for the needs of my body.

I have very early memories of just being in love with food. Food was such a big deal to me growing up that my friends and I even made eating a competition.

For years, we had a tradition of celebrating every single birthday at a buffet with my sisters and a few of my friends and we would compete over who could eat the most. Our goal was to eat as many plates as we could, and we kept track of our plates with sugar packets. One year, I remember I ate 7 plates full, so I had seven packets of sugar in front of me. I was already feeling so full, but I was competing to win so I got that eighth plate eaten and won the most food of anyone in the group. I was so proud but later, I remember laying in the back of my mom's car in pain and misery but feeling just so satisfied.

Of course, food doesn't fix emotion. It is not there to fix our boredom or distract us from life. The point of our get togethers is the people, not the food and food can't do any of the things we incorrectly eat it for. Food is for nutrition. If we are not hungry, or don't have a nutritional need, then we don't need to eat.

If we are bored, we need distraction. If we are lonely, we need to phone a friend. If we are distressed, we may need to talk or to walk or to get to the bottom of it all and decide to either let it go or fix the problem that caused it. We must get better about recognizing out real need and not trying to use food for the things it can't do.

We need to put food back in the place it should be in our lives. It supports our life. It is not at the center of it.

GET CONSISTENT

Healthy living for me used to be so black or white. I was either on or I was off. It had an all-or-nothing relationship with healthy living. I would set a goal for myself, then mentally fall off that track when something went wrong. I was ready to quit at every bump in the road, and when I was off, I really was off!

Healthy living just doesn't work that way. There is nothing healthy about alternating between an on again off again healthy lifestyle. Healthy living requires us to get consistent.

Before I could get healthy, I had to quit dangling divorce with that healthy lifestyle every time things didn't go the way I wanted them to. I had to quit being ready to break up with this healthy lifestyle anytime something went wrong.

it wasn't until after I had my second daughter Hayzlee that I made two major mindset switches that completely changed the relationship I had with food and fitness. I had to begin.

1) Eating the right foods for the right reason and
2) To change the way that I viewed food and fitness.

CHANGE THE WAY YOU SEE IT

First, I have to see that doing hard things was good for me. I had to learn that I really love that challenge. Doing hard things at makes you stronger, not just in body but in the rest of your life as well.

I had to begin to see healthy food as fresh and delicious and the best that there is, and I had to begin to see all the instant rewards I got out of fitness. I had to begin to believe I loved and wanted it in my life.

LEARN ABOUT NUTRITION

I have early memories of trying a lot of yo-yo diets with my mom. T and there was one night I was laying on the floor we were doing that all liquid diet and I was out of energy very young probably 12 and just lying there we had tried every fad diet out there and I remember I was still wanting to have treats even when I was cutting calories to the extreme so for example I was having that sugar-free Jell-O this is healthier at that time I didn't know a lot about the health benefits of eating certain foods and I thought that was healthy eating or not eating it all started one night when my husband and I were watching a documentary on Netflix called Fed Up This documentary with about sugar and how it's hiding in all of our food immediately after watch me I ran to my cupboards and pulled out a few things I was shocked how much sugar was in our pasta sauce baked beans and even in the stereo I was giving my daughter every morning it was protein Cheerios and I thought that was healthy but turns out there's 19 grams in one serving and the daily recommended amount by the American Heart Association is no more than 25 grams per day.

I now know that sugar is more addicting than cocaine. When you eat it, you just want more! When I started reading labeled and I started to eat for different reasons I began to eat for nutrients and health over taste.

BETTER NUTRITIONAL KNOWLEDGE

Better nutritional knowledge will change the way you eat because you will begin to think of the effects each food you eat is having on you.

As you go, keep researching different foods and build your personal library about what different foods can do for your body. I love to learn that adding a simple spice like cinnamon could completely spice it up. cinnamon is so packed full of antioxidants and there are tons of research studies showing how it helps you lower your cholesterol and other things like that, and it is so yummy on top of peanut butter banana cut up on I started to research different herbs fruits vegetables my mind was opened up to how powerful this food can be, and it really is Nature's medicine.

CHANGE THE WAY YOU THINK ABOUT FOOD AND FITNESS.

THE SECOND PART of a healthy body equation is to change the way you feel about fitness.

"YOU DON'T HAVE TO HATE THE PROCESS IT TAKES TO GET A BODY YOU LOVE." ~SHAELEE K. PHILLIPS

I used to struggle to get myself to workout. Now, it is my therapy and helps me burn my stress away.

I can't say I love it every day, but most days I get in the mood after I get started. If I'm still not in the mood I give it the best I've got for that day.

I have learned to look at fitness from a different perspective. When I am on a difficult hike, I imagine my grandma. I think about her being stuck to a chair the last 20 years of her life. I remind myself it is a privilege to move my body. I am so lucky I get to go on adventures and push my personal limits.

I used to dread working out. Now, it is my therapy. Fitness is my way to burn stress. In my old mindset, I had to fight myself to workout. Now, I look forward to it daily because I love the way it makes me feel.

This quote from Legally Blond always makes me smile.

Exercise gives you endorphins. Endorphins make you happy. Happy people just don't shoot their husbands, they just don't.

~-Legally Blonde

One of the keys to happiness in life is to learn to love those things that are capable of loving you back. Learning to love healthy food and fitness is something that will keep you healthy and help you love and take care of your body.

Finally, I had to learn that:

> "My attitude about this is my choice."
> This mindset changes not just your relationship
> with food and fitness, but it also changes your life. That
> attitude is how I am trying to live my life,
> and you may also decide that it is the way you
> want to live yours.

The motivation you have for working out comes from you and the way that you see it. If you want to change the way you feel about working or anything else in life, change the way you see it. That is the power of mindset.

With fitness, you can hate it and battle over it in your mind, or you can cultivate a different view of it that will make you love, want, and need it in your life.

Personally, I need to engage in fitness, b active, and eat right. They are part of my self-care. I need those things to help me feel the way I should about myself and my life. They help me get through things, feel good, and have a good attitude and the right kind of emotions in my life.

Removing the negative connection, you have with food and fitness in your mind. Court a love of it in your life. At very minimum, make living healthy routine, and refuse to let yourself suffer over it mentally in your head.

SUFFERING IS OPTIONAL

Bad things happen but suffering over them is always optional. Suffering can also be addictive and become a habit if we let ourselves do it too much. Suffering takes away your power, strength, and happiness if you let it take hold.

Sometimes we let ourselves suffer over our fitness or our perceived lack of physical power when there is no need to do so. Refuse to let yourself suffer over food and fitness in your life.

There are many alternatives to suffering over fitness.

1. You can turn off your thoughts and turn up your music (one of my personal favorites).
2. You can get up early and have it done before your head is awake enough to resist it.
3. You can think of it as your self-care routine, like I do. You can do this for your sanity and to take care of yourself.
4. You can begin to enjoy the routine by changing your perspective. Burn = muscles
5. As Mel Robbins says in the 5 Second Rule, you can 5, 4, 3, 2, 1, start moving.
6. You can set a personal challenge or competition to beat your personal best.
7. You can count or track things, like steps or days in row.

There are many ways in life that we can refuse to suffer and refuse to let suffering excuse us from other things in our minds. (Most excuses come with some form of self-pity)

Whatever you do, don't allow any of that 'poor me,' 'this is so hard' thinking that goes with suffering. Don't let yourself suffer over fitness. You have two other choices:

1. Just do it, (like brushing your teeth) or
2. Learn to look forward to and enjoy it.

With the right mindset, you receive an INSTANT REWARD from fitness the very day you do it. This comes from the way you feel about yourself and the energy level it gives you for the rest of the day.

Sure, it takes a little effort to get started. You just came out of a sleep. Your heart has been beating at a lower rate, and during the first five minutes, no matter how much you learn to love it, your heart rate needs time to get up to speed.

However, fitness and healthy eating are FULL OF INHERENT REWARDS. Luckily, when we learn to see these things the right way, willpower and impulse are no longer a problem.

- NOTICE WHAT YOU LOVE right now about fitness. Notice that you get a boost of energy, clarity, and happiness both during and after a workout. Notice how you suddenly must focus on your body and not your problems. And notice how much better you feel better as soon as you're done. The glow you get from that changes who you are and how you deal with the rest of your day, and the results last for hours.

After exercise, your stress goes down and your self-esteem goes up.

- Exercise affects the rest of your life; from the very day you do it. Exercise makes you stronger and happier in every way. It is not just about physical strength or what you will gain in the long run. Fitness makes you mentally and emotionally stronger now.

BECOME AWARE OF YOUR THOUGHTS

ABOUT EATING AND WORKING OUT

BECAUSE THEY DRIVE YOUR

EMOTIONS AND MOTIVATION

CELEBRATE SUCCESSES

Instant gratification is not a bad thing. In fact, it is a very powerful motivator. We just need to learn to use it right.
To get the power of instant gratification on your side instead of working against you, learn to *see the things you need to do in ways that makes them more enjoyable and easier to do!*

BUILD MOMENTUM IN YOUR LIFE BY CELEBRATING EVERY STEP YOU TAKE IN THE RIGHT DIRECTION AND MENTALLY LETTING THE ONES YOU DON'T GO.

CELEBRATE THE RIGHT THINGS AND YOU WILL BUILD MOMENTUM FOR YOURSELF IN THE RIGHT DIRECTION.

You can do this. You just need a mindset

that will help you get it done.

Remember:

You don't have to be great to start, but you have to start to be great."

– Zig Ziglar

WATCH YOUR WORDS

I am a huge believe in the power of words. The words you use in your head have a lot of power over the way that you feel.

1. Replace the words "should" with the words "want to."
2. REPLACE all the words that lead to DREAD with ones that create anticipation.

> "I always see this as a SELF-CARE ROUTINE I do for me. I want and need this, and I like the way I feel in my life when I do."

> In the right mindset, fitness RELIEVES YOUR STRESS, and makes you HAPPIER and FULLER OF ENERGY. Fitness makes you FEEL GOOD about yourself and better about your life. And choosing that kind of attitude about fitness and healthy food gives you the power to choose the way you feel about other things, too. There is a lot of intrinsic motivation you can activate here. You just have to change your outlook and focus on using the right words when you talk to yourself about it in your head.

Some words and concepts we think are just not good for us. Personally, I don't allow any version of the words 'don't want to,' 'can't,' 'too tired,' or 'low energy' in my vocabulary.

Much of the energy and motivation we have comes from the way we see things, and we are particularly susceptible to negativity in the words that we think. A word that it is a particular pet peeve of mine is 'EXHAUSTED.'

I still remember the day I discovered the power of that word, which got me started on recognizing the power of the other words I use in mind.

One day I noticed that whenever I thought or said the word 'exhausted,' it drained the energy and motivation right out of me. So, I banned that word in my life.

In general, we don't want to do the things we see as 'shoulds,' and 'have to's.' In general, we feel the way we tell ourselves that we do. Take away the words that hurt your energy and mood. They turn doing the right things into a battle that requires so much willpower.

The good news is your energy and motivation come from the way you see things.

IT DOESN'T TAKE MORE WILLPOWER

YOU JUST HAVE TO CHANGE

YOUR MINDSET

Get moving, get excited, turn on some music, and your energy will ramp up. Make it your reward and self-care.

Use powerful, motivating words like 'DETERMINED,' 'EXCITED,' 'LOVE THIS,' and 'GET TO.' Remove all negative thoughts and words like 'should,' 'have to,' 'I'm not good this,' and 'I have to do this because I am so fat.'

Words matter. The ones you use when you think about something make a huge difference in the way you feel about it. Use words that make fitness your reward and not your punishment.

PROGRESS NOT PERFECTION

The thing that defeats us is discouragement, and behind discouragement is expectation and perfectionism.

Sometimes perfection gets in the way of progress. When we are not perfect, things don't go the way we planned, or we don't get the results we expected, we can spiral into feeling less than and out of control.

Sometimes, we have to remove perfection and expectation so we can be free to be where we are and just make progress. Sure, we are going to slip, and we are going to fall. After all, we are human. We will fall. We will make mistakes, but we must also believe we are resilient, and we have what it takes. We will fall, but we can't let ourselves stay down their too long.

If you miss a workout or venture off track with your eating for a while, don't let that imperfection send you into a downward spiral that messes up your motivation and sense of direction or control.

Be vigilant about avoiding the negativity and discouragement that comes from not being perfect. None of us are, and discouragement and self-deprecation are the mental tools of self-defeat.

Allow MID-DAY RESTARTS

We used to throw in the towel until tomorrow when we slipped up in a day. However, slipping today doesn't mean you can't finish the rest of that day strong.

We used to let falling become a slippery slope, both mentally and physically. However, that logic is flawed. A mistake doesn't have to spiral you out of control. Allow mid-day restarts when you fall. Learn what you can from that fall to prevent it from happening again.

WHAT YOU DO WITH FAILURE

In your mind determines whether you will get

stronger or weaker when you fail.

FAILURE CONTAINS A LOT OF DATA.

You are missing out on all the value you can get from failure when you let yourself go down the slippery slope of self-pity and self-deprecation.

Of course, you are going to fall down. You are human.

That's just life.

But there is a lot of knowledge in that fall as well.

Where were you? What were you thinking? What was the situation? And how can you prevent that same fall from happening again?

Practice FORGIVENESS and focus on IMPROVEMENT. If something went wrong today, there is something you have to learn about yourself and your places of weakness that you can use to prevent it from happening in the future.

The KNOWLEDGE you gain from a fall is an invaluable part of your ultimate success. If you fall, you learn about another weak spot and failure point to avoid in the future.

Did you put yourself around temptation when you were emotional?

Did that mess up happen at a certain restaurant you went to with your friends?

- Maybe you could ask your waitress not to bring chips or bread to the table.
- Maybe you could eat at home before going out.
- Maybe you need to clear out the cupboards and get rid of junk food.
- Maybe you could bring a healthy side dish to share to the potluck you got invited to.

I always bring a large salad pack to have with whatever protein they are serving. I also love bringing fruit or veggies trays too. If I do want a burger at the party, I go for a lettuce wrap or only have one side of the bun. Now I never show up to a party empty handed. I always take water everywhere I go and a few healthy snack for the road because the kids and I get hangry!

The fact is, we are all going to slip up and fail. It is your view of that failure that determines the next steps. Will you beat yourself up or learn from it?

ALL failure comes with KNOWLEDGE. Life is saying, "Here is something about you and your weaknesses you need to know." If you can approach your own failure with FORGIVENESS and view it as an opportunity to learn what not to do in the future, every fall can make you stronger, smarter, and more determined to get there.

When we fail, there are two ways we can go,

1) Down that rabbit hole of despair which takes away all your power, or
2) Into that place where you analyze and learn about what went wrong and find determination to not fall down in that way again.

What you do with failure in your mind will determine what that failure does to you and your ultimate success!

Allow MID-DAY RESTARTS

You can have the magic of a new beginning in your mind any time you choose. You do not have to step onto the slippery slope of disaster every time you do something wrong. Instead, see the beauty and knowledge in failure because every time you do, you learn something else that is a part of the puzzle you need to succeed.

MAKE SMALLER MORE MANAGEABLE GOALS

Hopefully, you read my mom's chapter about Mailbox Goals. Sometimes we see the solution as bigger and more exact than it has to be. At first, it seemed like I never stuck with anything. Now, I am finishing 80-day workout programs and running half marathons, but it took a lot of baby steps to get there.

Fitness didn't work for me until I started making smaller more manageable goals.

I HAD TO RECORD IT AND MAKE IT VISUAL

Many people don't realize that I didn't get into this until after I had my second daughter. At that time, I realized I disliked the way my body looked, and I decided I wanted to get back on track.

At first, I set a goal of working out two days a week. It was a small goal, but you would be surprised how I would put it off. Little by little, the days would pass without me doing another workout.

Finally, I decided to hold myself accountable by logging workouts on a white board calendar in my kitchen. Every time I completed a workout, I gave myself a blue star on that white board. It was just a small visual reward, but seeing those stars made me work harder to get one.

I no longer need that kind of motivation. Now, I work out every day without fail because it is a habit and lifestyle, and I love it. But when I first started, I really did need that visual reward and accountability.

Now, I no longer reward or chart my progress. Instead, I wouldn't miss it for the world, but visualization helped me, and it might help you with accountability to break it down and make it visual.

We are all in a different place with our health.

You have to know where you are and find that level of support and motivation needed to take it to the next level.

To help you with this,

my mom and I now do **ONLINE COACHING**

and **IN-PERSON MINDSET RETREATS**

with us here in Utah.

I have helped people at all levels mentally and physically get on track. I have guided and coached people at all levels through some incredible transformations.

If you need help getting your head and body on the right track, contact one of us and we will be here to walk you through it. We all need different levels of support, and in this – WE'VE GOT YOU! Know where you are and COMMIT to get the help you need to take to the next level. We will be there for you when you do.

CELEBRATE SUCCESSES

As a coach, I've seen many people become discouraged because they don't focus on and celebrate their success.

People who start a new a new program with me often expect to jump straight into working out six days a week. When they put in only two or three workouts, they become frustrated with themselves and quit. The problem is two or three workouts was a success, not a failure. They didn't celebrate progress in themselves in a way that rewarded it. Instead, they saw failure where they should have seen and celebrated their success.

Success is incredibly validating and rewarding.

For someone who hasn't been working out at all, two or three days is a huge success! Celebrate that! No matter where you are, you've got to begin focusing on what you did right instead of what you did wrong. When you have a positive mindset, and you celebrate each step of progress, you GAIN POWER from that celebration. Focusing on the positive creates and builds momentum in the right direction. The power you feel from your success is what you need to become mentally and physically strong enough to get even better.

THE POWER OF SHOWING UP

You don't have to be great to start, but you have to start to be great."

– Zig Ziglar

JUST GET STARTED

More than half the battle of anything is in just showing up. We naturally pick-up speed in the direction we are going. What matters is not that you do something big, like we think we have to. It is that you just get started. Starting doesn't have to be intimidating. Sometimes it works better to start smaller and build some success. Every goal you achieve gives you CONFIDENCE. Each step you take in the right direction builds MOMENTUM. So, start with something small, like a 7-day challenge. If it's hard to get going, find a closer mailbox. Set smaller initial goals, and you lower the bar for the energy and commitment needed to begin.

Finally, show up and celebrate every step you take in the right direction.

Even when you don't feel like it, show up for that game.

Sometimes, you have to show up before your energy and motivation come around.

- Put on those shoes and get out the door.
- Push play on the remote to start that workout, even when you don't feel like you have the energy it takes.
- Just show up, and your motivation and energy will too!

DON'T COMPARE YOUR JOURNEY WITH OTHERS

Finally, don't compare your journey to the journey of anyone else. You have one life to live, yours. Focus on living your journey and don't compare your journey to anyone else's.

MY FITNESS HACKS:

CUTE CLOTHES

I don't know about you, but I love workout clothes. Buying some cute clothes to workout in makes it fun for me. Buying yourself some cool new workout gear, besides making it fun, is practical, too.

If you only have one pair of gym shorts or yoga pants, it's easy to skip working out because you haven't done laundry. It's not necessary, of course, but if it helps, wear something cute when you do.

Treat yourself to a few cute outfits, and you'll be excited for your next sweat sesh. I don't know about you but buying myself a new outfit to spice up my workout makes me excited to workout. It gives me an excuse to wear it!

PERSONAL REWARDS

Set up a rewards system for yourself when you complete a workout or hit a new goal. I used to get in the hot tub at the gym after a workout, and I would use that reward to talk myself into it. Think of something that will motivate and reward you when you reach a mailbox or when the workout gets tough, and you don't want to get off the couch.

FIND A BUDDY

Lately, I've been doing digital accountability with my team. We set up our phones or laptops and workout 'together' in our own homes. A workout buddy is an accountability partner. You might find motivation from having a friend to help keep you on track. The two of you can work out together, or you can just talk at the end of each day and discuss whether you both met your goals.

MAKE A PLAYLIST

Find some songs that make you want to move. Make a playlist of songs that make you feel good, have a good beat, and will keep you going while you work out. Music has a powerful influence on our moods, and one of the ways to ensure you enjoy your workout is by having some good music to play while you do. Increase your positive thoughts about fitness and decrease the negative ones. You control how you feel about fitness by the things you let yourself think about.

ELIMINATE NEGATIVITY

INSTEAD OF A NEGATIVE WAY TO SEE YOURSELF

AND THE PROCESSES THAT CHANGE YOU

NEGATIVITY DEVELOP:

- A love of fitness

- Gratitude for what fitness brings to your life

- And thankfulness for your ability to do it

The key to a better relationship with

your body is realizing that

you get to CHOOSE THE WAY YOU FEEL

about yourself, food, and fitness.

TO SUM IT UP

THE REAL KEY TO A BETTER BODY IS TO LEARN
TO HAVE A HEATHIER MENTAL RELATIONSHIP
WITH FOOD AND FITNESS IN YOUR HEAD

Change the reason you do it. Don't do it to be thin, do it to
be happy and strong. Learn to think about food and
fitness in ways that make you love and appreciate them.

Choose a healthy lifestyle, not because you hate the way
you are, but because you love that lifestyle and yourself
and you love the way you feel when you do it.

WHEN YOU CREATE A BETTER LONG-TERM
RELATIONSHIP WITH FOOD AND FITNESS YOU SEE IT
IN WAYS THAT SUPPORT THE GOALS YOU HAVE.

LEARN TO LOVE YOURSELF AND THE THINGS IT TAKES
TO GET YOU WHERE YOU WANT TO BE. BECOME A
PERSON WHO DOES AND LIKES IT IN YOUR MIND AND
DEVELOP A BETTER RELATIONSHIP WITH FOOD AND
FITNESS IN YOUR LIFE

ALL THE STRENGTH YOU NEED TO GET
WHERE YOU WANT TO BE LIE IN GETTING
IN THE RIGHT PLACE IN YOU MIND TO
REACH THE STRENGTH AND INSIGHT
INSIDE TO GUIDE YOU.

The Body Mindset

PART TWO

YOUR BODY MINDSET RETREAT

GET YOUR HEAD IN THE PLACE

IT TAKES TO GET THE BODY

AND LIFE THAT YOU WANT

The Body Mindset

CHAPTER

ELEVEN

BODY-MINDSET RETREAT

Your goal here is to disconnect, get present, tap into your own internal rhythms, and get into your mental place of power where things outside you do not affect you.

WELCOME to the day of your Mindset Retreat. This is the time to mentally and physical get back in touch with yourself, tap into your personal power, and commit to going in a new direction with your life and your body.

It is hard to change directions when you are mentally and physically going full speed ahead. A Mindset Retreat for putting your mind in the place it needs to be to tap into you're your place of inner strength, and resolve so you can see the big picture, decide where you want to go, mentally commit, and make a plan that will get you solidly on a different physical track.

Sometimes we need a mental makeover before we can find the power and strength inside ourselves to do something. We don't get into those places that make us powerful and decisive about where to go next when we are going full speed ahead in our lives. At times, you need to hop off the treadmill of life to get your mind and body back to where you want them to go.

THE LAWS OF INERTIA

As busy as our lives are, we are going a hundred miles an hour at whatever direction we are going. When we mentally and physically, start down a certain path, we pick up speed and momentum in that direction until we get stuck by inertia of the direction we're going.

We don't mentally turn things around and change directions on a dime. When we 180 in our lives at full speed, we often crash and burn with the body goals we say we are going to do.

By the laws of inertia, we need to slow down and put some effort into getting into a different mental place in our heads so we can make a turn onto a new direction.

We have the power to take our lives and bodies in any direction we choose. It's getting onto a different track and making that turn that is the problem. Our Mindset Retreat today is a day to make life around us come to a stop so we can that the decision to go in a different direction.

It is not really that life on that healthy track is so hard, it is that the turn onto it a change of course. Like any intentional change of direction, we make in our lives, it will take our intention and focus and attention to do it.

The mindset changes you are making today, will put you on that path. Today, you will make the decisions and commitments that will get you going in the direction you want to go. Before you begin to live on the necessary path to make a difference with your body, you must get in a personal place of strength and direction.

Today, you will do the mental work it takes to get your head back in the place of power and focus needed to decide what is right for you.

Today, you will get your head in the place it takes to make a change. Welcome to your Body and Mindset Retreat. Thank you for joining us today in a process that we believe will significantly change where you are with your head and body.

THE HOUSEKEEPING OF TODAY

Before we start, let's talk a little about housekeeping needs for today. In particular, let's talk about how you will eat and how long this will last.

Today's process is yours. You are in charge of every aspect of that process, including the length of time that is right for you to spend on each part. Most people seem to prefer a process that takes about 6 to 8 hours, but the goals are simply these:

1. To get back to a good and powerful place with yourself.
2. To make the decisions and commitments you need to do this from a place of strength and ability.
3. To make the plan that will fit into your life.
4. To physically prepare the food and clothes you need to make it easy and start strong in the morning.

That is the agenda for the day. The amount of time you spend on each section is up to you.

HOW TO EAT

You're eating goal today is not specifically about weight loss. It is about putting food back into its right place in your life. The way you eat today is up to you, but with the lack of distraction, it might be the perfect day to begin eating only when your body needs to.

The Pull System is a way of eating that allows our body to call for food with hunger and need instead of us pushing it in out of impulse, stress, or the habit to eat. The Pull System is a way of eating that returns food to a natural and healthy place in our lives by listening to your body's natural and healthy food-omitor, our own hunger.

Keep your head absorbed in YOUR GOALS and your mind off food until your body sends you the signal of hunger.

Today, and in general, keep you mind off food until you feel your own physical hunger. When you do, eat lightly from food that is good for your body. Eat just enough to appease your hunger so you focus and get back to the task at hand.

**KEEP YOUR MIND ON THE TASK OF TODAY,
WHICH IS TO GET INTO THE RIGHT MENTAL PLACE,
FIND YOUR PERSONAL POWER AND MAKE A DECISION AND
PLAN WITH THE POWERFUL IT TAKES TO GET THIS DONE.**

Today's schedule is up to you. Listen to yourself about how much time you need to spend on each objective. Read the book when you need to. Put it aside when you need to, and do what you need to do to get to the mental place you need to be in.
Today, eat to appease your hunger and take care of your other physical needs as you need to.
As you read today, stop, and take as much time on each section as you need until you feel you are at the place you mentally need to be.

ENJOY THE DAY

In addition, today is also about your enjoyment so,
LET YOURSELF RELISH AND ABSOLUTELY ENJOY THE DAY
Begin to anticipate the beauty of today. Your Body Mindset Retreat is a gift you give yourself. For most of us, the gift of a retreat to get us back on track is what we need the most.

Today, we step off the treadmill of our normal thoughts and actions to reach higher ground, find our bearings, and figure out where we want to go from here and what we need to do to get there.

Today is not just functional, it is also a rejuvenating and refreshing breath of fresh air needed to go where and become who you want to be. This much-needed retreat will put you in the mindset you need to be in. Today is a day for you, so relish in and enjoy it completely. Let this day refresh you and prepare you mentally and physically to go to the place you really want to be!

> NOTE: Training your mind to enjoy these days and do them well is a valuable skill that will dramatically change your life, effectiveness, and future experiences. A mindset of enjoyment and effectiveness is critical to a better life.
>
> To reach the right mindset, look in the mirror and have a short morning meeting with yourself every day. Every day, before you begin have a mental meeting with yourself and

COMMIT TO TWO THINGS
1) Commit to being happy, and
2) Commit to being effective.

Commit to going to bed that night one step closer to your body goal, no matter what things happen outside of you that you can't control.

While a morning meeting with yourself may seem like a small change, it will make an intense difference in both your effectiveness and the way you feel that day. The morning meeting you have with yourself each day will be the best 30 seconds you ever spent.

Wake up and decide you are both going to be happy and effective that day. Decide where you want to go and that you will be effective and enjoy doing it. This is not just a Body Mindset skill, but a mindset skill that will radically improve your whole life.

You are doing this Mindset Retreat for the purpose of putting yourself back together mentally and physically. You are here to get your head around getting back on the track you want to be on. Today could be one of the most memorable in your life because it is the day you do something meaningful to change your mental and physical direction. Today is a much-needed gift you give to yourself. Get in the mindset it takes to relish and enjoy this experience.

Start your retreat.

LET'S BEGIN

FIRST, SETTLE IN

Lay or sit somewhere you can be relaxed, comfortable, and ready to settle into this experience.

Close your eyes. Relax, breathe deeply, and picture yourself checking into your own personal one-day retreat. Envision a place of peace and beauty where you instantly feel a lightness in the air. The vibes of the place you are walking into let you know that this is a where you will be enlightened, find yourself, and have clarity you need to go in a new direction.

Today is a day of introspection, enlightenment, and focus. It is a day to get back to the center of who you are and decide who and where you want to be. Not only will today feel good, but it will also get you back on track and you will leave with the vision and powerful, calm resolve it takes to go where you want to be.

The purpose of this retreat is to shift towards a healthy path with your body. Since changing your mindset impacts many parts of life, this retreat is about getting back to the place you want to be in general. Your Body Mindset Retreat will help you get back in touch with yourself and figure out where and who you want to be from here.

PART ONE – FIND YOUR SILENCE

TUNE INTO THE SILENCE AROUND YOU

BE STILL AND LISTEN

TURN OFF THE NOISE

Your first objective of the day is to turn off the noise. We fill our world with so much noise and busyness that we can barely hear ourselves think. Even when we are alone, we turn on the TV, listen to music, watch YouTube, or zone into our phones. We so often fill the silence with other people's thoughts and noise that we are unable to hear or get in touch with who we are. Not only that, but we also have noise going on in our own heads as well.

It is not that sound is bad. The artists and authors of our world give us so much inspiration and much-needed entertainment. We just need to turn it off from time to time so we don't let the thoughts of others conceal our own.

Our lives get so full of noise and busyness, that we sometimes can't hear the inner voices that guide us. It is during these times that we understand who we are and what we are doing. We desperately need to hear our internal voices that guide and help us effectively and uniquely be who we are.

Your first objective of the day is to turn off the noise, sink into your surroundings and ground yourself. We can't go where we need to be on the inside until we stop the chaos and noise both inside and outside of us. Slowly unwind and tune into the silence in you. Progressively begin to reach a place of quiet inside your head and peace within yourself. As you do, get more and present in you as you reach for that place of calm inside of you. Eventually, you will make the decisions and commitments you need to make for your body. For now, ground yourselves and find your mental place of peace, strength, and control.

As the noises in your head begin to quiet, you will begin to hear noises in the room around you. That is part of becoming completely present. Notice the noises you can hear around you. Is there complete silence or are there ambient noises in the room? Be still for a while. Sink into this place. Simply observe. You need to be completely present to see things as they are and decide how you want them to be. Progressively begin to reach that place of stillness and peace that will put you back where you need to be.

Settle into silence. Be still, grounded, and present in the place you are in. Let your mind and body leave the treadmill they have been on. Begin to shift your mind back to a place of peace and strength that you will need to move forward from here.

Take some time to be physically frozen and mentally still. Silence the voices and begin to hear and feel the rhythms of life around you. As you become completely quiet, a part of you inside is waking up. You don't have to make this happen, it just does this as you become still and settle into complete awareness of the place you are in.

What ambient noises do you hear in the room around you? Do you hear traffic or people around you? Notice them rushing around in their daily lives, focused on what they are doing. Do you hear the noises of the infrastructure that keeps you warm or cool? Sink into complete stillness and observe. Even in silence, life is abuzz around you. Let yourself be aware of activity around you, but calm and still inside.

Become Fully Present

Sink more into the silence or sounds around you. Become fully present in the place you are in. Observe the room in a way you seldom see it. Become intensely grateful for the place you are in. Put the book down. Turn off the sound, breathe deeply, and simply enjoy. Give yourself time to fully settle in and enjoy the peace and quiet of the place you are in. Take this time to find your center and become completely aware of your surroundings.

Spending some mental time with yourself this morning lets you discover that you can feel good in your own skin when you really settle into it. Being fully present is a place of calm. The deep waters of your mind are always where your joy and comfort lie. They are not in external places where we frantically search for them. Stop and enjoy how good it is to be mentally and physically present with yourself.

In this place, you make your best decisions, feel your best, and are most authentically happy and in charge of yourself. Silence is a gift, and you are giving yourself that gift of that silence today. Settle into your own peace and silence and spend some much-needed time here.

Become Physically Still

With mental stillness comes physical stillness. When our minds are racing, our bodies are moving. Your muscles are tensing. Your foot is moving. You don't settle fully into your chair, and you are not fully present in the room or with the people around you. Your mind is abuzz, and your body is moving. As your mind slows down, your body begins to slow down too. You become fully present in this room.

In this state of stillness, you can not only hear noises in the room, but you also begin to have the mental stillness to hear and tap into the inner voices that guide you. With mental and physical stillness, you accept the place you are in and you do not try to gloss over life by pursuing multiple tracks at once.

Often, until the paralysis of sleep sets in, our minds and bodies seem to always be racing. In this state, our sleep becomes a fitful attempt by our minds to piece together the mess it is working on during the day. When we have not reached a place of inner peace, even our sleep is not as restorative.

When you become still, your mind stops racing, and you start really living instead of glossing over life. When your mind is racing, you are in a state of near constant need. You reach for food, shopping, activity, distraction, or something to help you fix what your mind and body perceives as stress. Much of the food that we eat is an attempt to feel still inside and mentally at peace. Often, when we think we need food, we simply need the air that we breathe and to find our internal deep water.

Let your body fall into that completely still place of paralyses you reach right before sleep, but as it does, keep your mind awake and enlightened. If you feel sleepy, don't recline. Your body should be nearly in the paralysis of sleep, while your mind is intensely awake, clear, and at peace.

This is a place of meditation. It feels intensely good and refreshing to be here. Relish the lack of need and the lightness and completeness of full mental presence. Be still, relax, and observe.

APPRECIATE THE LUXURY

Appreciate the luxury of being still with no need to move at all. Appreciate the absence of mental noise and physical motion. Appreciate the calm of deep water that lies inside you. Even when the surface of life is rough. You can deal with things so much better when there is a place you can go to inside yourself for relief. We come here to reach our peace. Don't reside here but let the calm of this place permeate the way you handle life.

TAKE IN THE OXYGEN

Breathe deeply, feel your body relax, and settle into the space you are in. Our bodies need more oxygen than our lungs give them when we are tense or uptight. We can't sink into our space until we get the air that we need. Right now, you need nothing but the air that you breathe. Let yourself feel and enjoy the absence of need. Relish being alive, the feelings of life in your body and the peace of being mentally and physically still.

You may want to take this meditation deeper today. If you do, continue into a deep state of gratitude. More fully sink into the chair or bed you are on and become intensely grateful for its presence here to hold you. Be completely grateful for the roof over your head, and the heating and air that controls the temperature around you. Even the humblest of abode can be filled with more peace than the most elaborate, and everything can be appreciated more when you tune in to the place you are with full gratitude. Have intense gratitude for being here and this experience today.

Begin to widen the gratitude you feel toward the people in your life. Think of someone in your mind and become intensely grateful for that person in your heart. Decide to value and do justice to that relationship in the future.

Gratitude meditation can be lifechanging. Take a moment now to focus on the gratitude you have for your own abilities. Be grateful for your own insight, intuition, and ability to see things the way you choose to see them. Be grateful for the strength of your resolve. Your daily gratitude meditation doesn't need to be time consuming. It can be focused deeply on only one person or one aspect of your life.

The time you spend here is yours to choose. Take this experience as deeply as you'd like. Take time to marvel at what you are, and do, and have. When you reach a deep sense of gratitude, bring the focus back to your body.

MARVEL AT THE LIFE IN YOUR BODY

No matter the shape of our bodies, the life in them is a miracle. You are alive! Become aware of and relish in the life in your body.

Can you feel life pumping through your veins? Can you fill it filling up your lungs rhythmically? Become overwhelmed by and get in awe of life. Life is a miracle. Begin to feel the flow and rhythms of life in your body. Feel the slow and steady rhythm of the way that you breathe. Relax completely. Let your body pull in breath only when it needs to. Letting your body breath and eat only when it needs to, is respecting the natural rhythms of nature as they should be. Letting your body pull in air and take in food only when your body says it needs it, is beginning to listen to and respect the rhythm of nature over the overly excitable and anxious rhythm in your thoughts or head. Your body's need for oxygen and food is based on its activity. If you are still, your breath is slow and steady. Breathe according to your body's need instead of the way you breathe when your thoughts are racing.

This is the natural rhythm of life. Between these breaths, you may feel the rhythm of your heartbeat or the blood pulsing through your veins. You have life in your body! Feel and relish in the life inside of you.

As you settle into your own rhythm, separate yourself from the need for everything else. Truly, at this moment, all you need is the air that you breathe. Right now, the air and silence you have is more than enough. In fact, this air and silence is filling you up and bringing intense joy.

Separate yourself from the need for everything else that normally drives you. You have life, silence, and time with yourself. This is the best gift of all. Need is frantic. Life is full!

As you become aware of the sound of silence and life around you, realize that the peace you have felt today is often drowned out by the racing, chasing, and pursuing state of your mind.

It is intensely empowering to realize that peace is always inside you when you need it. Before you can even begin to hear the internal voices that guide you, you must remove all the internal and external noise that block them out.

CONNECT MORE DEEPLY WITH THE SILENCE

Connect more deeply with the silence. Finding your own center requires complete stillness. As your body slows down to its natural rhythms, you reach a place of peace and a sense of ease and enlightenment in the stillness around you.

Today is your day. It is a day to slow down and get in touch with yourself. As you come down from the rat race, return your focus to your room, yourself, your body, and your growing sense of peace and contentment with things just as they are. You have life and the air that you breathe. That is all you need to feel like this! Today, silence is one of the gifts you are giving yourself.

Connect with your physical body. Feel the life-giving oxygen as it enters and leaves your lungs. Your body is here right now, and it is alive. Listen to the sound of life coursing through your body and develop an intense gratitude for it. You have the breath of life inside you. You can see it, you can feel it, and for now, you need nothing more than the air you breathe. Appreciate the gift of life and let that gift be more than enough. Right now, there is nothing you need except this place and the beautiful and peaceful air you breathe.

We begin pushing food in and other destructive or nonproductive things when we operate from a rhythm that is not our own. We reach for destructive or distracting things when we are in a mental place of need and 'tensation,' the sensation we have of stress and tension in our minds and bodies.

We rarely take the time to feel our bodies or be aware of the life we have inside us, and that it is a luxury to do so. Put this book down. Give yourself some time to exist in silence and tune into your body and surroundings. Then, have the intense realization that all of what you need is always inside you.

We lose sight of the fact that our hearts are always beating. Our breath is always cleansing our body. Our blood is carrying life giving oxygen through our veins. We get so wrapped up in our problems and our heads that we forget we have the magic of life in our bodies.

Let yourself feel and really appreciate the life you have flowing through your body. In how many ways can you feel the rhythm of the life inside you now?

Can you feel your stomach processing food inside you? Can you feel the muscles in your forearms with blood coursing through your veins? Become aware of your hands and feet.

TURN YOUR FOCUS INWARD

Now, it is time to turn your focus inward to who you are when you are most authentically you. It is time to tap into your strength, vision, kindness, and strength.

In the busyness of life, we can lose sight of who we are. You have the physical feeling of life inside you, but you also have strength behind your resolve and the uniqueness of you. No one in this world, brings exactly what you do to it. Of all the things you have done, what brings you the most pride? At your heart, where no one knows you but you, who are you? What does it mean to be you when you are in touch with yourself? Who are you when you are authentically at your best?
You are determined and resilient. When you want something, you go after it. What have you accomplished that required strength? What have you wanted and pursued? That strength is an important part of you, and it is there for you to harness and channel. Allow yourself to feel your strength. When you want something badly enough and are determined, nothing can stop you. Tune into that strength and let yourself feel it for a minute. You can do hard things when you buckle down and get in the right mindset to do them.

Now, strip away your accomplishments. What if you had to start again? Who are you without who the world thinks you are? Who are you when you are most authentically you?

Now, focus again on your breath and the feelings of life in your body. You have life. You can feel it coursing through your veins. You can feel life in the beat of your heart if you listen for it. It is in the rhythm of the breath that brings oxygen into your lungs. Experience what it means to have life and exist separate from others and the thoughts, pursuits, and emotions that normally drive you. Feel the luxury of just being alive.

Realize that right now you don't need anything at all, but the air you are breathing. This air is cleansing your body and providing the oxygen to regenerate your cells. Be still. You have breath and you have oxygen. You have everything you need. You need only the bed that supports you and the oxygen you breathe. You don't need to move or think. Just be alive and aware of your body. Find your center. We are always chasing something, but it actually feels good not to chase anything. Separate yourself from the things, accomplishments, and people you normally pursue. Enjoy simply existing, whole and complete without the pursuit of anything. Life is very simple. It is us who complicate life. You lose sight of its simplicity when you get wrapped up in the pursuit of things.

FIND YOUR STRENGTH

Who are you without your pursuits? Who are you aside from the people you have or want in your life? Tap into your own personal and inner strength. Find the strength of your own resolve? Find the strength that comes from knowing what you need and what you know it right?

Listen for and feel the strength of the intuition and spiritual voices that guide you. What do you know to be true? Who are you at your core What strengths can you draw on in this pursuit? Find the strength of your own inner decision and tap into the strength of the resolve you have when you finally know and decide what you are going to do. Tap into the strength you have when you are in your personal place of inner strength.

EXIST IN THAT SPACE

Turn your thoughts back to your physical existence. Feel your head beating. Feel the rhythm of your natural breathing when your body calls for oxygen out of need as it should.

Just exist in this space, for a while.

Can you feel the rhythm of your own energy flowing throughout your body? How does it feel like to be completely still? Let your mind, quit chasing the things, people, and achievements and emotions you are normally change and just live. Relish the idea of just having life going through your body.

Be still, Be completely here, and in the moment, fully aware of yourself, your life, your rhythm and full present and aware in the place that you're in. Feel safe. Feel aware. Let yourself listen and feel and be at peace with yourself and everything else for as long as you need. This is your sanctuary. Right now, nothing else matters but you getting to the place of perfect peace. This time is for you. Relish it. Breathe and spend some time in this life and power giving place of depth, awareness, and peace.

The length of time you spend here is up to you. If you need or want to spend more time to feel fully at peace, do so. This is meditation. It is veery beneficial to your mind and body to turn everything off for a while to recharge and get back in touch with yourself and he powers that guide you.

CHOOSE TO CONTINUE OR MOVE ON

If you feel ready, you can skip ahead to Part Two - The Personal Care Section of this book, or you can continue taking it deeper on the next few pages ahead.

Listen to yourself and your needs. If you feel fully strong and powerful and refreshed, and you are back to the place of power you need to be in, you may choose to move on to the personal care section of your retreat. If you have not fully checked out and got above the challenges of your life, take more time to tap into the energy and power around and inside you.

Begin to Listen

If you are staying with us in meditation, begin to listen to the sounds around you. Are there noises you rarely hear? Can you hear the lives of others around you? Do you hear traffic or the sounds of the house? Picture people rushing to work or doing whatever they are doing, involved in their lives, as we all usually are.

Do you hear any of the sounds of nature? Whether you hear them or not, the birds are there, living life from their own perspective. Think about the bigger picture. We are often so wrapped in our own lives that we are unaware of others.

Return again to the thoughts of your body. Breathe deeply this time and expand your chest and stomach slightly to draw more cleansing oxygen into your lungs. Think of the oxygen going into your body. Think of the clean air coming in and the oxygen coursing through you veins, removing the impurities from your body. Allow yourself to sigh deeply and relax. Now, become completely still between each breath. Sink into it until your body needs another cleansing breath, then sink again, into the absolute stillness of your own body.

Listen to your rhythms again and slow them down. Slow your breathing. Feel your heartbeat slowing as your body needs less and less. Become still. Take the time to slow down, become quiet, experience peace, and just feel. Then, when your body is calm, listen to your thoughts.

THIS IS YOUR RETREAT
Today is your day. It is a day to listen to and reconnect with yourself. Listen to the timeframe of your body's rhythms and needs. Let today fill your needs and put your back where you need to be.

There is much knowledge in your body. In the right mental place, we feel peace and timelessness. In the right mindset, we do things well and are not at rush. In the right mindset, we see the big picture and we are always more than enough. Let yourself be that and get to that place in your mind.

When you get to the right place with meditation, you feel enlightenment. Some people describe it as tingling, warmness, or glow. Others say it feels like lightness or that suddenly everything seems to make sense. You will know it is time to begin the next phase, because it will feel like you have finally found your center. When you do, slowly get up, get present and begin to take care of your body.

HOUSEKEEPING
Just reminder to try to stay hydrated today. Drink water whenever you arise. Replenish your water every time you get up to go to the bathroom. Today, stay hydrated and listen to the physical needs your body has for food. If you feel hunger, eat. If you don't, get your focus fully back on the task at hand. Today is a good day to begin to eat for the real needs of your body.

If at any time today, you feel stress or you lose focus, return to the simplest and most powerful luxury we have, the gift of life itself. Return your focus to the experience of life within your body.

During the first phase of your focus retreat, you have become aware of silence, you have found and gotten in tune with your own rhythm, you have found your center, and tuned into the inner strength you will need for your journey. Now, connect yourself to this feeling in a way that that will help you recreate it any time that you need to.

RELISH AND MARVEL AT THE LIFE IN YOUR BODY

Become aware of the life within your body. You are alive! Can you feel life pumping through your veins and filling up your lungs? Become overwhelmed by the awe of life. Begin to feel the flow and rhythms of life in your body. There is a slow and steady rhythm to the way you breathe. Relax completely and let your body pull in breath only when it needs it. When you let your body breathe according to its needs, it does so at a slow and gentle rhythm, unlike the way you breathe when your thoughts are racing.

This is the natural rhythm of your life. Between these breaths, you may feel the rhythm of your heartbeat or the blood pulsing through your veins. You have life in your body! Feel and relish in the life inside of you.

As you settle into your own rhythm, separate yourself from the need for everything else. Truly, at this moment, all you need is the air that you breathe. Right now, the air and silence you have is more than enough. In fact, this air and silence is filling you up and bringing intense joy.

Separate yourself from the need for everything else that normally drives you. You have life, silence, and time with yourself. This is the best gift of all. Need is frantic. Life is full!

As you become aware of the sound of silence and life around you, realize that the peace you have felt today is often drowned out by the racing, chasing, and pursuing state of your mind.

It is intensely empowering to realize that peace is always inside you when you need it. Before you can even begin to hear the internal voices that guide you, you must remove all the internal and external noise that block them out.

AWARENESS, AND A CALM CENTERED PLACE WILL BE YOUR SUPERPOWER IF YOU CAN FIND AND REACH IT. IT IS THIS MENTAL PLACE THAT WILL GIVE YOU THE STRENGTH AND COMPOSURE YOU NEED TO BE HAPPY AND ACCOMPLISH YOUR GOALS

Become present by tuning into your body and deciding to fully enjoy the people and world around you. When you become truly aware of how your body feels, you will begin to feed it when it needs food and will quit eating when you are not hungry. If you simply do that, you will never be fat again. Also, get out of your own head and come back to earth, where real happiness lies. Don't live in a blur. Develop an awareness of your body and surroundings.

One reason that vacations are so refreshing is they get you out of your head and make you become fully present. Live your life as if you were on vacation. Notice the sun, wind, and rain. Connect, laugh, listen, and enjoy your family, friends, and even the strangers around you. Take a hike and only stop to eat when your body says you must. Enjoy your body and your appearance. This is your life. You might as well love it. Develop a state of 'with-it-ness' and connect with your true self.

Trust me, when you are really connected to your body, you will look 10 years younger and feel 20 pounds lighter because you will hold your body as if it matters. When you have 'with-it-ness', people may say that you glow or that you look really happy. People will be drawn to you and want to be around you.

It is by living in the moment that you will experience the most joy and look and feel your best. It is by being fully aware that you will eat for the right reasons and make the best choices for your body. Cultivate the quality of being truly present in everything you do. Open your eyes to the joy of keeping it real.

FIND YOUR PLACE OF STRENGTH

We all have a mental place in which we are strong and competent This is the place you must be in to do things competently and well. To get there, think back to times you have been in touch and in your place of mental strength.

Get into your personal place of strength in your mind. From your place of strength, you have what it takes to approach anything you do competently and well. Before you make you set your goal or make a plan to change your body, get into your mental place of strength so you can get effective with that and do it well.

ANCHOR THAT FEELING

Create a physical sensation or a simple gesture that will serves as your anchor to this mental state you are in. creating an anchor can help silently and invisibly bring your back to this place of calm and inner strength when you need to be there. Create a small and personal signal to tie you to this place. It should contain a physical action but be small enough to be done anywhere, unnoticed by others.

I suggest anchoring this feeling by touching your thumbs to your middle fingers and breathing deeply for 30 seconds, touching two fingers to your sternum, and feeling the air enter your lungs as you take a deep breath or squeezing and massaging the pressure point between your thumb and first finger, while relaxing your shoulders and breathing deeply enough to extend your stomach.

Shaking your head or rubbing your face can also help you clear your mind and return your focus. Try all three and see which anchor feels right for you. To further anchor your center, focus your eyes on an item in the room and let that item signal a sense of calm in your body.

In my room, I have two. One is a blue lotus blossom on top of a lamp given to me by my daughter. The other a family picture I have hanging on my wall. These are visual triggers that help me return to this place later on. Anchoring this feeling with a simple physical or visual sign can help you more quickly get back to your place of calm later on.

SPENDING TIME CARING FOR YOUR BODY AND PHYSICAL APPEARANCE SENDS THE MESSAGE THAT YOU AND YOUR BODY ARE WORTH BEING VALUED, RESPECTED AND CARED FOR.

The Body Mindset

PART TWO – PERSONAL CARE
CARING FOR YOUR BODY

Your goal during this part of your retreat is to get in touch with your physical body, experience luxury, and take care of your appearance in a way that says you are beautiful, and your body is worth it.

Physically caring for your body sends you the message that your body matters and is beautiful. As you care for and experience luxury in your body, you get better in tune with your body, and you develop the love and admiration of it that sends the message that you and your body are worth this kind of care.

Feeling beautiful and valued helps you become fully present in the body you have. When we don't feel good in our bodies, sometimes we don't value or care for the way that we should. By experience luxury today and indulging yourself in self-care that makes you come out looking and feeling the best that you can, you send a powerful signal to yourself that you are important and that you matter. This part of your retreat is the luxurious personal care of your body.

It will include a luxurious soak in a world of bubbles or with a scented bath bomb, exfoliation, care of your nail, toes, teeth, and hair. Then spend some time styling your hair, applying makeup (if you use it) and dressing in something that makes you feel the best you can in the body you have.

We treat your bodies best when we are present in them and not stuck in a world of trouble in our minds. ***The self-care portion of your retreat will put you back in charge of yourself and your body and will leave you feeling that you are powerful, and your body is worth it.***

When you become truly aware of and in tune with your body, you will begin to feed it when it needs food and not when it is not hungry. Get in tune with your bodies need for food and you will l never be fat. One reason to stay in tune with your body is to start listening to its need for food. Another reason to get in tune with your body, is that it gets you out of your head where unhappiness lives and present with life where real happiness lies. Don't live your life in a blur. Get grounded in your strength. Develop a better awareness of your body, and get fully present again in the life that you're in.

A MINI VACATION

Think of this part of you retreat as a mini vacation for your mind. One reason that vacations are so refreshing is they get you out of your head and make you become fully present. Live your life as if you were on vacation. Notice the sun, wind, and rain. Connect, laugh, listen, and enjoy your family, friends, and even the strangers around you. Take a hike and only stop to eat when your body says you must. Enjoy your body and your appearance. This is your life. You might as well love it. Develop a state of 'with-it-ness' and connect with your true self.

Trust me, when you are really connected to your body, you will look 10 years younger and feel 20 pounds lighter because you will hold your body as if it matters. When you have 'with-it-ness', people may say that you glow or that you look really happy. People will be drawn to you and want to be around you.

EXPERIENCE LUXURY

Recognizing you can give yourself luxury in your life can be EMPOWERING and lifechanging! Recognizing that you can make yourself feel better and give yourself the experience of luxury without money or anything outside of you gives you power over your own personal experience. It is essential to realize you have the power to give yourself luxury and get feeling better on your own when you need to.

Experiencing luxury in your mind can take away the deprivation from which many of our mindset problems occur. Deprivation makes us feel sorry for ourselves personally which can lead us to justify all kinds of bad body behavior, including things like drinking and overeating. Seeing that we have the power to experience luxury and feel peace gives us power over our own experience that can take away all that escape we do into the wrong things in our lives.

In the right mindset that luxury can be from the right soap or by lighting a candle, turning on some music and taking a bath. Luxury is a mindset. Some people need to spend a lot of money to feel it, if they do at all. Others feel it when the sun shines on their back or the wind blows through their hair.

When you feel like you have connected with yourself and are back in your own place of peace and personal power, it is time to enter the second part of your personal retreat. This is when you physically care for and focus on your body. First, as a matter of housekeeping, remember that today is about comfort. If you are physically hungry, eat something light, preferable with some protein and a little fat and/or fiber, but only eat when you physically need food. Also, continue to replenish your water supply after you visit the restroom.

PHYSICAL CARE

Tuning into your body and caring for it helps you prepare for your body goals by returning your focus to your body. When you cleanse, exfoliate, and care for your body, as you might in a luxurious spa, it sends the message to your brain that you are worth it. Your body can look good, feel good, and is worth putting effort into. Caring for your body helps you focus on your body, which is what you need to start this process. Caring for your body also increases your blood flow, speeds up weight loss, and improves circulation.

When you spend some quality-time taking care of your body and appearance, you are more likely to value it enough to make good choices and reach your goals.

PHYSICAL CARE

Physically caring for your body sends you the message that your body matters and is beautiful. As you care for and experience luxury in your body, you get better in tune with your body, and you develop the love and admiration of it that sends the message that you and your body are worth this kind of care.

Feeling beautiful and valued helps you become fully present in the body you have. When we don't feel good in our bodies, sometimes we don't value or care for the way that we should. By experience luxury today and indulging yourself in self-care that makes you come out looking and feeling the best that you can, you send a powerful signal to yourself that you are important and that you matter. This part of your retreat is the luxurious personal care of your body.

It will include a luxurious soak in a world of bubbles or with a scented bath bomb, exfoliation, care of your nail, toes, teeth, and hair. Then spend some time styling your hair, applying makeup (if you use it) and dressing in something that makes you feel the best you can in the body you have. We treat your bodies best when we are present in them and not stuck in a world of trouble in our minds. ***The self-care portion of your retreat will put you back in charge of yourself and your body and will leave you feeling that you are powerful, and your body is worth it***.

When you become truly aware of and in tune with your body, you will begin to feed it when it needs food and not when it is not hungry. Get in tune with your bodies need for food and you will l never be fat. One reason to stay in tune with your body is to start listening to its need for food. Another reason to get in tune with your body, is that it gets you out of your head where unhappiness lives and present with life where real happiness lies. Don't live your life in a blur. Get grounded in your strength. Develop a better awareness of your body, and get fully present again in the life that you're in.

YOUR MINI VACATION

Think of this part of you retreat as a mini vacation for your mind. One reason that vacations are so refreshing is they get you out of your head and make you become fully present. Live your life as if you were on vacation. Notice the sun, wind, and rain. Connect, laugh, listen, and enjoy your family, friends, and even the strangers around you. Take a hike and only stop to eat when your body says you must. Enjoy your body and your appearance. This is your life. You might as well love it. Develop a state of 'with-it-ness' or state of being fully present with your body, and your life and connected with your true self and the energies that give you strength and knowledge from inside.

EXFOLIATE AND LET THE BLOOD FLOW

When you take the time to physically care for your body, it helps you become more present and tuned into its needs, but there are also physiological benefits for caring for your body.

When you exfoliate and care for your body, you get the blood flowing to your skin, muscles, and areas that contain fat deposits. This blood flow is necessary to losing weight, skin rejuvenation, nourishing tissues, and building muscle. All of life's physical processes require blood flow. Blood brings nutrients that nourish and provide the building material for lean muscle. It also transports carbon dioxide and other waste out of cells to the area of exchange, like the lungs. Blood flow in fatty areas speeds transport as fat is broken down and used for energy. Exercise also speeds up blood flow.

Cultivating blood flow to your tissues helps speed up the process of weight loss by increasing the blood needed to convert fat to energy. It brings oxygen, protein, and other nutrients necessary to build muscle and speed healing. Blood flow is necessary to all body systems. It also makes you feel good by increasing the endorphins that improve your mood, and when you feel good, you handle both your hunger and cravings better.

SELF CARE ROUTINE

I strongly believe that when you care for your body the way you should and make it look the way it can, you value and are willing to take better care of it.

Our job is to fully appreciate and connect with ourselves inside and out. Caring for your body helps you connect with and prepare to take better care of it. It tells you that you are worth it. It also feels good, gets the blood flowing, and makes you feel better about the way you look.

After you connect with silence and your own strength, it is time to get up and take a luxurious bath. Allow your body to soak in the warm soapy water, so you can soften and remove dead skin cells. Use that time to get yourself into your Body Mindset. This is your body, care for, celebrate, and revere it. Promise that you will take better care of it from now on. Connect more deeply with the physical and mental parts of who you are.

As you go, exfoliate your body to remove dead skin cells and stimulate blood flow through your body. Remember fat loss requires blood flow, as fat must be liquified and carried away by your blood. Fitness also gets blood moving to remove unwanted fat. Water and blood flow are necessary to liquify fat and break it down for energy.

As you care for yourself, you should continue to build your mindset, resolve, and focus for your plan.

Focusing on areas of your body that may need special help encourages blood to rush to these areas. This will help to speeding up weight loss and reduce sore muscles. Also, focus on the dead skin and calluses on your hands, feet, knees, and elbows. Shave your legs, if you'd like, and deeply condition your skin. Finally, if your hair is dry or in bad condition, this is an excellent time to do a deep conditioning or oil treatment. Then, when you have finished bathing, dry yourself thoroughly, exfoliating with the towel. You may want to use moisturizer or lotion to leave your skin smooth and lightly scented.

When you are done bathing, brush your teeth. Focus on your teeth more than you normally do. Floss each tooth very thoroughly. You may want to use a makeup mirror to remove everything. Use mouthwash so your mouth feels clean, fresh, and ready to begin anew. Then blow dry and style your hair and apply makeup if you use such products.

EXPERIENCE LUXURY AND PEACE

Experiencing luxury in your mind can take away all that deprivation that make us feel sorry for and justify ourselves. In the right mindset that luxury can be from the right soap or by lighting a candle, turning on some music and taking a bath. Luxury is a mindset. Some people need to spend a lot of money to feel it, if they do at all. Others feel it when the sun shines on their back or the wind blows through their hair. Today is a day to allow yourself to reveal in the luxury you can create for yourself in today.

How often do you feel luxury? Luxury is something you get to revel in, appreciate, look forward to, and enjoy. How often do you look forward to something and then relish in it when you get there?

We don't let ourselves experience luxury often enough because we feel like we are too busy, and that luxury must be expensive. Luxury can be free. Luxury can be a cup of tea you enjoy alone or with a friend. It can be a beautifully laid out breakfast of berries and cheese or a candle lit while soaking in the tub. You have the power to create luxury around you every day if you choose.

The first part of your retreat is the luxury of time and the second part is the luxury of body. During your mindset retreat, allow yourself to feel the luxury of the day you and recognize that today is the day you get in touch with yourself.

Your mindset retreat is divided into two parts: mind and body. First, you to get in touch with who you are and what you want. Then, you give yourself the luxury of self-care and grooming like at an exclusive spa. If you choose, you could go to a day spa or get a professional pedicure during the self-care portion of your retreat, but don't lose sight of the real reason for your retreat, which is to get in touch with and value your own body.

Allow yourself to enjoy each step of the process. We rarely give ourselves the luxury of time, and today you are taking time to focus on your body and mindset. Don't allow yourself to worry about time as you normally do. Today is about removing that pressure and focusing on what you can give yourself simply by deciding to do so.

You may also choose to add a special touch, like scented candles or soft music. Today is your very special retreat. Enjoy the luxury of taking care of your body and preparing for a new adventure.

As part of your self-care routine, strive to make yourself look and feel as good as possible, both mentally and physically. When you feel good about yourself, you feel more valuable and worthy of the time and effort needed to take care of your body.

Start your plan with a body and mindset routine by spending quality time focusing on yourself. Spending time on yourself, your mindset, and your body will help you get in the right frame of mind to care for your appearance and improve yourself.

When you are more aware of your body, you are more likely to value it, listen for real hunger, and care about the nutrition and fitness your body needs. Taking time to care for yourself increases the value you place on your own appearance and health. Making yourself look groomed and beautiful creates a sense of inner peace, focus, and contentment that will be central to your body mindset and fuel your progress.

THE POWER OF INERTIA

Inertia is a natural law of science and physics that says an object in motion stays in motion unless acted upon by an outside force. Your Focus Retreat was like the outside force influencing your course of motion. By participating in a Focus Retreat, you can use the force of your mind to get yourself back on track and moving toward your body goals.

Remember, change is always hardest at the beginning. It takes the greatest amount of effort to overcome the friction of sitting still. That is why you need everything else to come to a stop to put your full effort towards putting your body back on track.

Plan on some resistance as your body adjusts to a new level of eating and activity. You are retraining your habits and what you are used to. It will take a little work to get your body accustomed to a new level, but it will be worth it. Switch into a powerful mindset before you change tracks.

Change is hard. Once you are on a new track and become accustomed to eating or performing at a different level, it won't be so hard to stay there. It is like the law of inertia that a body in motion stays on course unless acted on by another force. Be a force of change for yourself and as many others as you can.

Most struggle and effort of change comes at the beginning. After the effort of getting on track, it is far easier to stay there. If you establish powerful and easy routines, before you know it, your body will adjust, and you will settle in. Everything gets easier because as you go on, your ability to do so increases.

In your first few days, you will ask your body to do what it's not used to doing, but as you advance, this will become the new normal and things will become easier. At that time, you will have changed course and be solidly on a different track with your life and body.

That inertia is much like the one you have been traveling on until now. You have been moving in one direction. Your Focus Retreat is the force of change. Before an object can change direction, there must be a moment when it comes to a complete stop. This Focus Retreat is the moment of stillness between one path and the next. Tomorrow, you will begin a whole new path, in a whole new direction. Today, everything about your crazy life (and I assume that because it has become the case for far too many of us) gets to come to a complete stop so that you can prepare and focus before you jump back in.

Your Focus Retreat is the time for you to stop, refocus, and readjust so that you will be ready to begin mindfully in a new direction. If you don't take time to prime the pump for change, you will simply be trying to add the components of a new diet or fitness plan on top of all your other pursuits and thoughts. If you're not ready for it, a diet will become just one more thing in a cluttered space. Without taking the time to be mentally prepared and ready for change, you will be far more likely to fail.

GET FULLY PRESENT

A purposeful trip into your own head is a necessary and powerful way to gain clarity and focus. However, we spend a lot of unproductive time in our heads, as well. Sometimes, instead of being fully present, we get caught up in the past, our worries, or our negative emotions. When we do this, we are too removed from our lives and decisions, waste precious time, and make our worst decisions.

Some planned time for our thoughts is a good thing, but ultimately, we need to work on becoming fully present, enjoying reality, making the best decisions, and connecting with those around us. Use the time wisely, and tomorrow try to really see and enjoy the things and people around you.

It is when you are purposeful and real that you make the best decisions for you and your body. Strive to become more present so you can properly care for your body.

THE EXPERIENCE YOU HAVE HAD TODAY
HAS CAUSED YOU TO BECOME MORE MINDFUL

We spend far too much of our time in a self-absorbed and emotional state of mind that puts us out of touch, out of control, and without full enjoyment of our lives and path. When we are too much in our heads, on our phones, or on anything else that makes us not fully present, we do our worst eating and make the worst choices.
When we are in our heads, we are not living fully, and there is no way we can truly enjoy or connect with others, life, or our objectives. When you are wrapped up in other things, you are only half here. Therefore, you are unable to experience the real joy of connection to the things and people around you.

When you spend too much of your time in your head, your life goes by in a fog. Sadly, it is also one of our many habits. If you have gotten used to being wrapped up in your own thoughts, Netflix, a book, Facebook, or the Internet, there is a good chance you have the habit of not being fully present.

While these things can be enjoyable and distracting, (which does help with cravings) they also take you away from being 100 % connected, which is where you experience the joy of living. When you are not fully present, you don't notice the smell of fresh cut grass and colors lose their vibrancy. When you are in your head, you don't communicate deeply or authentically enough to know people, and you eat and act in a mindless way. These things take away too much of your life. No wonder you think you don't have time to be active.

One of the saddest things is if you are distracted, you are not the active driver of your vehicle. You can't drive down the path where you want to go if you are reading a magazine or sitting in the backseat. You are far less likely to experience happiness or anything real when you are fogged by other pursuits.

So, for your diet or body pursuit, we need to be fully present, and it is often harmful to our goals to be too much in our own heads?

Being wrapped up in your own problems or in a bad place in your head,] can cause you to eat mindlessly. It's easy to fall back into old eating habits when you are not actively in the driver's seat in your life. Additionally, you don't enjoy or really taste the food you eat, so you feel far less satisfied from it.

Second, since you don't fully enjoy or connect when you are in a mental fog, you also probably feel like you are missing something. You are, of course. You just don't know what, and instead, you tend to seek out things that are not good for your body or mind, like junk food, excessive eating, or even alcohol or drugs. You know you need something; you just don't know what it is. Often, the choices you make when you are not fully present are not the best ones for your body or mind.

Finally, when you are too much in your own head, time goes by in a flash, and you feel like you don't have time to fit in important things like your workout or connecting with others and building relationships. Chances are there is wasted time in your day that does not add value. Eliminating things that don't matter can give you back all the time your need for the things that do.

Actively living in a present way requires us to slow down. When you are running through life with so much speed, you lose touch with what really matters, and while it may feel like you are getting a lot done, we are not very effective when we are going in a thousand directions at once.

When we slow down and become more mindful of what is important and necessary, we can achieve more important things. Being purposeful helps us focus on what matters. Slow down and focus on eating foods that are necessary for our bodies and enjoy them as you do. Love your workouts and be fully present in them and with anyone who joins you.

Put your mind back into life, and it will help you accomplish your goals with real purpose, thought, and enjoyment. When we quit spinning our wheels and become purposeful, we accomplish more and have a fuller life.

Today, you are becoming mindful. We live too often in automatic loop of habit without awareness. Here we often act and reacting without awareness and we don't take care of ourselves the way we should. Take some time to become more aware of yourself, your priorities, and your surroundings. Don't waste time or mental energy on things that are not important. Today, recognize that we find joy and purpose and make the best decisions in our lives when we are most fully present. Set a goal of becoming more mindful in everything you do but be gentle with yourself and do it gradually. Remember that your mindfulness is also a habit and give yourself time to reach that goal as well.

Gently get better at being completely present in whatever you do and in tune with the needs of your body. Gently get better at finding and staying in your personal place of strength and not in your emotions.

Remember that this place is inside you and know that you can come back to it anytime you need to. The anchor you learned can help you get back to this mental place quickly when you need to.

.

HOW TO END

You can end the focus and body portion of your Mindset Retreat whenever you feel you have slowed down and are in a good place mentally. Take some time to record your thoughts and your resolve before you move on to the next step, which is making a clear plan of exactly what to do so that you can jump back into life and without requiring decisions. When you are ready, and you have written your thoughts and insights, move forward to the stage of clarity and planning.

Tomorrow, as you rejoin the normal world, your goal is to be physically and mentally ready for a new track with your body. As you move forward, remember the commitments and focus you found today. It will be the source of your power and energy. Make this new beginning in your life memorable.

Get this feeling in your head. It is the place of strength, clarity, and focus you need to move ahead. Remember, any time you fall off track, you can stop for a moment and bring yourself back to the way you felt when you first made a commitment. Focus is something you can give yourself any time you need.

A TIME TO WRITE

Now, write your thoughts, feelings, commitments, and plan. Grab a pen and cement this time into something real for you. Right now, while you feel clear and focused, you can use that clarity in the most powerful way. When making the decision to change your life, this is the time for insane clarity. You need to know exactly what you will do and how you that will look. Too many people make important life decisions when they are not in the right headspace to make them. Write what you feel, even if it has nothing to do with your body. Remember that this book is simply a tool for you to accomplish your goals.

MY THOUGHTS

Reflect on what you have learned about yourself and where you have decided to go with your body.

_____

_____

_____

_____

_____

_____

_____

_____

_____

_____

_____

_____

_____

_____

_____

_____

_____

_____

_____

_____

_____

WHAT'S NEXT?

The next chapter is about gaining the INSANE CLARITY you will need on your journey. You may want to take additional time to write. After that, you have two choices:

1. SKIP AHEAD TO PHYSICALLY PREPARE FOR TOMORROW
       OR...
   2. CONTINUE TO IMPROVE YOUR CLARITY THE FOCUS
      YOU NEED TO GET THERE.

NEXT UP: INSANE CLARITY

Now that you know what direction you want to go, you got into the mindset to make it happen, and you made a decision in your mind that is powerful enough to get it done, it is time to create a plan that is so clear and easy to understand and follow that you will use to get it done. When you create a plan that is so easy and insanely clear that it can become routine in your life. You will create a plan with do-ability and sustainability it mind. Designed to fit into your life so you will be much more likely to follow it.~

A GOAL WITHOUT A PLAN IS
NOTHING MORE THAN A
WISH

The Body Mindset

CHAPTER

TWELVE

INSANE CLARITY

When you get insanely clear about what you want, and insanely clear about what it takes to get there, you will be insanely more likely that you get where you want to be.

The Body Mindset

Why insane clarity? Isn't regular clarity enough? The problem is we always think we are clear about what we want and what we need to do to get there. Then in the thick of things we find we are not as committed or clear about what we are going to eat or do as we thought.

When you get insanely clear about what you are going to do, insanely committed to doing it, and insanely clear about exactly what you are going to do each day to get your there, it becomes insanely easier to follow that that plan until you get where you want to be. The clearer your objective and the process is in your head the more likely you will be able to get it done.

> Now is the time to take your goal from vison to design. Now is the time create the routine and the eating / fitness plan it will take to get it done. It is time to clearly understand when you will eat what, at what time you will work out, what workout you will do, and when and how that will fit in your life. It is time to get insanely clear about the plan you will follow to turn this goal into reality.

GET INSANELY CLEAR ABOUT WHAT YOU WANT

When we start out, many of us are not as clear as we need to be about how long we are willing to do this and where we expect to be by then.

Do you remember the chapter on mailboxes? Well, the mailboxes were my short-term step goals along the way, but I knew my overall objective was to get to school before a particular event.

Not only was I insanely clear about where that next mailbox was so I could focus on it, I was also insanely clear about my overall objective and the timeframe I had to accomplish it.

THE BIG PICTURE

What are you trying to achieve overall with your body? How much do you want to lose? (if you do) and what will success look like when you get there. For me, ultimate success happened the day my BMI (body mass index) fell back into the normal range for my age and height. Success in my body goal was very clear. The second I am no longer 'overweight' as measured by my BMI, I win. Of course, I still wanted to improve after there, and I did, but mentally, I had already won. Winning, as I defined it, was no longer being 'overweight' or 'obese' as measured by the system my doctor uses. I had close to 100 pounds to go to get to a healthy BMI, well maybe 80 or 90lbs to get there, but I knew what I had to do, and I gave myself one year to get there, and I did. My second major goal was to run a half marathon. Winning at that goal was crossing the finish line, with any time at all. I also wanted to run a lot of it if I could. Success lied in crossing that finish line and I did, having run .

WHERE IS THAT WIN?

At what moment do you say, "I just did it." At exactly what point do you cross that finish line and say, "I won!" The first thing to get insanely clear about is where that win lies for you? That could be a number of pounds you need to lose, an amount of time you are going to do it. (For example, I will stay on course until school is out this summer so I can be ready for swimsuit season this summer. The day you win is the day you make it summer vacation with maybe 6 out of seven perfect days each week. (you choose your exact measure of success.) When you win, you are going to go out and buy that new swimsuit.

What is that clear win? How long do you have to get there? What ae you going to do and feel when you do? (Your reward could be something concrete, like the swimsuit, or the intense pride and emotional reward you get from doing it.)

Get clear about exactly what you will call 'the win,' how will you know you got there and what will do when you do?

_____

_____

_____

_____

_____

_____

_____

_____

MAKE THE COMMITMENT

It is time to fully commit to making this happen in your life. Take out all your backout plans for failure. Get rid of the 'I'll tries' or 'As long as it's not too hard's.'

It is time to sit down, wrap your head around your goals, and mentally commit to get there with enough power and commitment to ensure that you do.

Committing to do this doesn't mean you know exactly what will work. It means you won't quit going at this and modifying make it work yet, only that you will find a way.

When JFK committed to going to the moon, he didn't have any idea how we were going to do it, yet only faith that we could and determination that we would. He made a commitment on faith that baring none, we would do this thing, and that somehow, we would do what it takes and figure out how we were going to get it done.

Take some time to mentally wrap you head around this and commit doing whatever it takes until you find a way to get it done.

Rate your level of commitment to achieving this goal? How determined are you on a scale of 1 to 10 to stick with this goal, learn as you go, put in everything you have, and find a way to get this done?

1 2 3 4 5 6 7 8 9 10

(circle one)

JFK drew a line in the sand and said one way or another, we will cross that line How committed are you to put in whatever it takes to ensure that you cross that line you set for you?

_____

_____

_____

WHAT WILL IT TAKE TO GET THERE?

JFK's speech called a lot of people into action. After that speech, I can just imagine the buzz that went on at all level of NASA. Suddenly, a whole lot of people had to sit down and come up with a plan that would make this work.

And of course, there would not be just one plan. They would learn and try and modify and rethink it time and time again until they could find a way to get it right.

While you might get lucky and find what works for you the first time out it is far more likely that you will have to try a number of different things, scrap many of them, come back to the drawing board, and figure it out again.

You will also have times when you feel like quitting.

And times you do it when it will be hard to do.

YOU MUST PERSONALLY DESIGN A PLAN

After years of doing this, I have found that we often do best when we personally design the plan.

Sure, you can buy a published diet or follow an old tried and true and that should work just fine, but you know your likes and dislikes and your personally challenges and limitation better than anyone out there. You know that obstacle course of your life better than anyone else.

If you job or your spouse requires that you eat out 5days a week, you will make a plan where you can find success within those parameters. If you have little kids you have to feed and take care of, you need to make a plan within that set of circumstances.

Your schedule, your times of stress, your likes, foods you don't handle well, and many other things can be taken into consideration on a plan you make and customize to your life.

We often find a diet or a plan that worked for someone else, and we try to bend ourselves and our lives around it. We take a plan that work for someone else and try to make that fit our lives and help us accomplish our goal when our goal and our lives are like no one else.

We are individuals. We can't make an 'until death do us part' commitment to a plan that is inflexible or not customized to fit our lives.

One of the reasons you will be creating your own plan today instead of me telling you what to eat is you much more likely to be able to follow a plan that we create. When you create it, not only does it take your likes and challenges into account, but you must also create a plan that will fit your life, and you mentally buy into it when you do.

CREATE A PERFECT DAY ON PAPER

After you have made a JFK ,eve, of COMMITMENT to reach your goal, your next step is to sit down, like those engineers must have done after that speech and put your brain on this. "Okay, if I'm going to do this, what will it take to make this happen?"

Create a routine and a plan, which will be the maps and blueprint that will get your from where you are to where you want to be.

The first step is to know what a perfect day in that plan on paper. Exactly would that day look like>. How would it work? What would you eat and do? How would that fit into your life on a regular day? Write this perfect day of your journey down on paper and make it completely clear in your mind.

Once you clarify what a perfect day would look like on paper, it always amazes me how much easier it is to get up and follow that plan in your life that next day.

Of course, it's not easy, especially if you are doing a 180 in your routines and direction. It may still be a challenge to challenge your body with something new, but it is easier because with clarity, you know and can anticipate and get ready for exactly what is coming nest. You don't have to wait know what your next meal will be or where and when you will have it. All you have to do is get up and follow that insanely clear plan of what a perfect weight loss or fitness day looks like to you on paper.

Get clear and surprisingly, that goal finally fits into your life. For some of us, real clarity changes the game so much that it makes us successful even if we never have been before.

OOPS, NOW WHAT

OR HOW DO YOU SEE A SLIP?

During the process of achieving our body goals it is inevitable that we will slip and fall. Part of making that really clear plan is to plan what to when you fall.

What you do mentally with failure will determine if you gain the inevitable learning and ultimately the strength that comes from knowledge from it or if it will defeat you and sends you mentally and physically spinning out of control.

It is inevitable that we will fall in this or whatever we do. Seeing a slip as a failure or letting it say something negative and global about you is a slippery slope that will mentally defeat you or cause you to spiral out of control.

A big part of success is what you mentally do with the failure in that process! Expecting perfection often makes you breakable. If you let it, even one step in the wrong direction leads to that slippery slope of self-loathing and justification for melting down and stuffing your face full of food. Failure can be a slippery slope that makes you mentally spin out of wrong direction if you let it.

What you do mentally with failure is even more important than what you do with success.

More ability, dreams and goals are defeated by discouragement than any other thing. To stop yourself from that tendency we have to mentally spiral out of control, we must do a better job of mentally handling our failure when we fall.

When you fall, don't allow discouragement. Instead, see the learning that is inherent in that failure. Discovering a danger point and is discovering another piece of the puzzle about what works. If you waited too long to eat, and spiraled out when you did, don't get that hungry again. If you overdid a portion, prepackage it, or don't cook that much. If you couldn't resist the candy bowl, get rid of the candy bowl, and don't allow any more of that junk in your reach.

One thing I've learned from my own failure is when I am stressed and my mind isn't in the right place, I am in real danger of blowing my eating if I have the opportunity to do so.

The solution for me seems to be to take away the opportunity to eat anything more than rabbit food during stress.

Another thing I had to rather reluctantly admit is there are certain foods that I can't manage well. One of these is break, especially with butter. I had to learn to tell the waitress not to bring the break or chips to the table before dinner or I'll eat it. Now I know that:

> IF YOU CAN'T EAT A FOOD WITH GOOD CONTROL
> YOU SHOULDN'T' BE EATING THAT FOOD AT ALL!

I had to eliminate some foods from my life just because I don't manage them well. Because of failure I know that eating or being around food when I'm not in the right mindset, is too dangerous.

Failure is full of data if you get out of the place where you are mentally screaming at yourself inside so loud you can hear or learn what that failure is trying to tell you.

NOW CREATE AN INSANELY CLEAR PLAN OF ONE PERFECT DAY

When we are not clear, about what to do it all seems so hard. When we become insanely clear about the process the things we are trying to do becomes insanely easier to do.

Before clarity, our battle was twofold, deciding what to do, and doing it! Take away your lack of clarity and you can simply focus on execution. Make an insanely clear plan and you are working off a list.

Eat this breakfast .... CHECK, I can do that!

Drink this much water... .... CHECK.

Get my 30-minute workout out of the way ... CHECK.

Eat the sweet peas and pepper sticks I packed when I get hungry ...... CHECK.

Check my step count and walk a little more to get it where I want it to be by lunch... CHECK!

Be carful around 3:00, my danger zone....CHECK!

Eat the dinner I planned... CHECK.

No more eating after 7pm... CHECK.

Make it to bed and I did it!

INSANE CLARITY ALL THAT AMBIGUOUS STRUGGLE AND ROOM FOR ERROR OUT OF YOUR PLAN. An insane level of clarity makes it just execution.

Just one perfectly planned day and executed day is often the difference between success and failure because you have to know what the target is before you will ever be able to hit it.

Take the time to create and plan that one perfect day today. Planning it is not scary or intimidating. Even if starting this psyches you out, get it on paper. You can start mentally agreeing to follow it better if you know exactly what it is you are committing to do. Besides, you can repeat that a perfect day over and other again until you can create and commit to the next one. We don't have a lot of time, creating one perfect day is reasonable.

Planning a perfect day gives you clarity. Executing one gives you power. After you know what it is, commit to following that plan for one perfect day. You can make it to bedtime for one perfect day if you focus on it. Put everything you've got into achieving that one perfect day and your confidence and sense of direction will change because you do.

GET COMPLETELY CLEAR WITH WHAT YOU WILL EAT AND DO, WRAP YOU HEAD AROUND THE THAT AND ACCEPT THE COSTS OF THAT GOAL. PLAN AND COMMIT TO ONE PERFECT DAY AND THEN UP AND FOLLOW YOUR PLAN. .

Make a plan and get it on paper for three reasons:

1. **Before you can accept the costs, of your goal, you need to know what they are**. When I buy a car, I won't even go look at it if they won't show me a price. It always makes me thing that their prices are something they are embarrassed about and they must be too unreasonably high to show. When we don't know exactly what that body goal will look like in our lives, we also think it will cost too much. Getting insanely clear about what that day looks like lets you begin to wrap your head around that day and accept the cost and challenges of it.

2. **We don't' make good decisions under pressure**. When we are hungry or stressed or our minds are wrapped around the details of our day, we have no focus left for good decisions. A decision of what we are going to eat made under stress will likely not be a good one. Making those decisions ahead of time, takes away that impulse eating we do when make eating decision during our times of hunger, stress, and pressure.

3. **We can take advantage of the power of routine**. Every human being is programmed to automate their life with habit and routine. Getting clear about and trying out one day of that lets us begin to solidify part of that into repeatable patters that will ultimately form a life. By doing that one good day and committing to repeat it, we begin to build the habits on which all healthy living is based. To become sustainable , healthy living much become a habit.

The sooner we can make it routine, the sooner it can get easier to do.

Part of our body goals being so hard is that is requires our active thought and us to make good decisions under pressure. We can take all that away when we pre-decide and pre-accept that this is what we are going to do tomorrow. When our minds are full, we often fall back to something simple. Make it clear. Make it simple to do and remember. Plan and commit to the detail of the diet and fitness it will take to be successful and you will far more likely to stick with it until you are.

Here is a sample way to start your day:

- Wake up

- Spend 5 minutes mentally committing to and reviewing your plan

- Brush your teeth...

- Drink 16 oz of water...

- Do a video workout (or run, or go the gym or whatever you do)...
- Shower
- Eat a spinach, mushroom, egg, and cheese omelet.
- Take veggies and a salad and ½ cup of carbs for lunch.
- Leave for work.
- 10 am – snack on sweet peas and carrot sticks.
- Drink some water.
- 12:00 eat my salad and ½ cup of carbs.
- Drink some water.
- 3:30 snack of celery and peanut butter with raisins or an apples and raisins.

- Get involved in a project that will keep me busy because this is the time of day, I will make it or break it.
- 6:30 dinner of vegetable soup, lean protein and a salad and some sugar free herbal tea.
- NO FOOD AFTER 7PM

Knowing in advance exactly how that day will go will take away all the minute-by-minute decisions you often have to make to stay there. Getting insanely clear makes it nothing more than compliance. Get there and you can keep your mind off food and make it to bed without messing it up.

Lie in bed and let myself feel really good about making it through today before I go to sleep.

GET UP AND REPEAT

MAKE A PLAN THAT IS POWERFUL, YET SIMPLE ENOUGH TO GET THIS DONE, then simply get up and repeat until you need to modify to make it more effective. .

My own rules are simple:

No Sugar

No Flour

No simple carbs – like starches

No liquids that contain calories

And

No food after 7:00 pm.

I can eat:

UNLIMITED non-starchy vegetables and

UNLIMITED lean protein when I'm hungry.

Note: In general, we eat too much protein because we are so anti-carb, but I find the promise of unlimited food helpful to overcome the fear of being hungry, so I don't limit protein at first.

After my initial carb detox, I allow two carbs per day, three or more when I'm training, and no-carbs (except vegetables) when I hit a weight plateau.

> No simple carbs – sugar, flour, or starchy foods
> Two servings of complex carbs per day, both eaten with protein and containing high fiber.
> And no carbs at dinner

Exceptions

Drop to one carb per day if you are struggling to lose weight.

Add a carb if you are training, male, breastfeeding, or quit-heavy when you begin.

Remember you have a unique metabolism (the level of fuel efficiency you need to run). Those with very small frames, due to age or genetics, or whose bodies have a low metabolism (are very efficient at getting miles out of the food they eat) need less to maintain their weight or tip the scales toward weight loss.

Your food equation is unique to you, so work with your body until you find it.

Fruit is good for you but needs to be limited because it has a high sugar content.

Artificial sweetener is not good for you but use it if you need it.

Hot liquids, like broth, fill your stomach when you are hungry.

Fresh vegetables are unlimited and can help with snacking especially if you cut them up to make them appealing and convenient. 100 calorie packs of nuts (I especially like cocoa covered almonds) can give you fat and protein that will stay with you. Just be careful to limit the quantity, which is why I like the 100 calorie packs.

Sugar-free gum can help with stress eating by curbing cravings for something sweet.

LACK OF WATER IS THE CAUSE OF MOST OF OUR CRAVINGS. Our bodies are used to getting a portion of their liquid from food, so we often crave food when what we really need is water.

Water is necessary to the chemical process of breaking down fat. When your body thinks its hungry, it is often actually thirsty. Drink water and wait 20 minutes to find out for sure.

TIP TO GET ENOUGH WATER: drink a tall glass of water upon rising. Then, replenish what you lost every time you go to the bathroom. REMEMBER: *Talk to you doctor about all your nutritional needs AND* supplements. I take probiotics, omega 3's, vitamin D and iron when I need it.

WANTS VS. NEEDS

Learn to sperate your food wants from you needs in your mind.
EARN SOME OF THE FOODS YOU WANT WITH ACTIVITY
and GIVE YOURSELF THE FOODS YOUR BODY
ACTUALLY, NEEDS FOR FREE
If you are really craving something, you can earn it by working off the equivalent number of calories with physical activity. It is amazing what things you no longer want once you see the price tag attached.

ONLY EAT WHEN YOU FEEL PHYSICAL HUNGER.
The next tip that is a real game changer: begin to use hunger as nature intended it. It is like your body's gas gauge that tells you when you need food.
We never overfill our cars. We use instruments to detect when they need it. That is what hunger is to us.
If you properly use your hunger as your gas gauge,
you will never have a weight problem.
Don't just eat because the clock says it's time to eat. Don't just eat because it looks good. Eat because your body needs fuel. That doesn't' mean you can't eat something that looks good, just wait until you are hungry to eat it.
It is incredibly important to learn to listen to your body's actual need for food. The people who get good at listening to their body's need for

food and feeding that with healthy things never have a weight problem.

> Feeding your body, the right foods when it
> is physically hungry and not feeding it
> when it's not the key to your goal.

Losing and maintaining weight is much simpler than it seems. Just eat the right foods, for the right reasons and in the right amounts.

MAKE YOUR PLAN

Now, it is time for you to sit down and a create a plan than you will follow every day to get you where you want to be.

This space is your own. Use it to plan what you are going to do and how you are going to do it. Just like your budget, the first step to making this work is to clarify what it will look like in application. To begin, use these pages to make a plan that includes what to eat and do each day to make it happen.

CREATE A PERFECT PLAN

REMEMBER YOU CAN DOWNLOAD A FREE, MORE COMPLETE WORKBOOK AT THEBODYMINDSETBOOK.COM

To live a perfect day, you need to get insanely clear about what that looks like. Lay out a plan for one perfect day that includes what time you get up, what time you meditate and get your head on straight for the day, when you work out, and exactly what you eat and when you do it. Like a blueprint to a house, outline one perfect day in great detail.

_____

_____

_____

_____

_____

_____

_____

_____

THE POWER OF DISTRACTION

Now, think about what we have learned about the power of distraction. Make a short list of things you can get mentally and physically wrapped up in that would distract you when things get hard?

_____

_____

_____

PREDICT AND PREVENT PROBLEMS

Finally, predict what could go wrong.

You've likely been down the road in the past. What has mentally or physically stopped you then? Are there thoughts or distractions that get you off course? Is it discouragement when you don't get the results you thought you would? Do you eat worse with family or friends or when you are alone with food? Do you excuse going off track for: Celebrations? Emotion? Chaos? Or Stress? How has the physical proximity to food you shouldn't have affected you?

What have been your roadblocks been in the past?

Now, create a plan to prevent that from happening again.

_____

_____

_____

_____

How has not being prepared with the things you need played a role? Do you have workout clothes and shoes? (if you use them) Is the food you planned to eat there and easy to eat when you need it, or is the wrong stuff closer and more convenient for you? How can you fix that?

_____

_____

_____

_____

How has impulse, eating affected you? What can you do mentally and physically to prevent that?_____

_____

_____

_____

What excuses or challenges often cross your mind? In other words, what you blame it one when you go off track in your eating or fitness?_____

_____

_____

What role does your own emotion play in this? How can you 1. Fix your emotion (by changing what you think about or how you see something?) 2. Prevent yourself from hurting your diet when you do feel negative emotion? _____

_____

_____What other challenges do you have personally that make this hard for you? (list personal or physical challenges that make it especially hard for you right now or always)_____

_____

_____

_____W

hat can you do despite these things?_____

_____

_____

What other challenges do you predict? Birthdays? Stressful situations? Challenges at work or in a relationship you have or anything that is coming up that may challenge the success of this goal?_____

_____

_____

Now make a plan to prevent you losing it at birthdays, or work parties or any of the stressful times you predicted could be a problem.

_____

_____

_____

_____

_____

Make a plan for eating out. What places are safe for you to go because you know a menu item that is compatible with your goal? What will you eat off that menu? You may need to do a little research to build you list of 'safe' places to eat in the future.

MY EATING OUT PLAN

_____

_____

_____

_____Is there anything you could safely eat from a fast-food menu if you needed to?

_____

_____

_____

_____

What can you tell the waiter or waitress that could protect your diet form failure while you are there? (For example, Don't bring the bread or chips to the table, I'd like that on lettuce instead of bread etc.)

_____

_____

_____

Also, remember to daily:

1. Set your commitment in the morning.
2. Break it into mailboxes when you need to (For example I just need to get through the last hour to make it to lunch or bedtime without eating)
3. Use self-talk to coach and keep yourself on track throughout the day.
4. Then use Instant Emotional Reward throughout the day, whenever you do something right. Reward the heck out of yourself with the best kind of emotion and pride you can let yourself feel to shape your behavior with positive reward.

KEEP IT POSITIVE AN D GIVE YOURSELF TIME TO ADJUST

REMEMBER TO REWARD WHAT YOU DO RIGHT AND

LEARN FROM AND LET GO THE PARTS YOU GET WRONG

Transitions to a new physical direction take time. Be gentle and encouraging with yourself as you make that transition. Give yourself a break when you slip up and mental and physical time to adjust to better on a better track with your body.

Remember that it gets easier. Be patient with yourself when it feels hard, or you get hungrier that you think you can handle at first.

- Drink plenty of water.
- Fill up with broth or herbal tea or other sugar free hot liquid.
- Try sugar free gum.
- Get bulk from veggies and low or no grain vegetable soup.
- Keep busy and your mind off it as must as you can.
- Create a mailbox to make it to when it gets hard.
- Allow unlimited veggies and lean protein when you need it.
- Remember it takes 20 minutes to fill satisfied after eating.

If you crave sugar, try sugar-free gum or diet soda (neither are great for you, but we often need to do these things in baby steps so find some no calorie solutions if you are struggling with the loss of sweet.

Here is a sample meal plan you could follow every day until your tired of it. Of course, this is just a sample. It us up to you to create an effective plan you like and can eat with control and reason.

NOTE: A PORTION OF OUR FAMILY IS VEGAN, SO I ALWAYS INCLUDE A VEGAN OPTION.

Sample Meal Plan　　　　Sample Vegan Meal Plan

Breakfast #1	Breakfast #2
Spinach omelet – a big handful of spinach, onions, sliced tomatoes, and a sprinkle of cheese topped with one egg.	High fiber, low sugar maple flavored oatmeal with pecan and chia seeds, topped with blueberries and coconut milk.
Snack	Snack
½ cup granola w/ sugar-free or plain Greek yogurt	1/2 sliced mango and 1/2 banana
Lunch #1	Lunch #2
High fiber wrap with lean chicken, a sprinkle of cheese, spinach, tomatoes, arugula, green salsa, and basil-balsamic olive oil.	High fiber wrap with black beans, ½ cup brown rice or quinoa, tomatoes, green salsa, arugula, and basil-balsamic olive oil.
Snack – 1oo calorie cocoa covered almonds	Snack – 1oo calorie cocoa covered almonds
Dinner #1	Dinner #2

Oven baked citrus ginger salmon and teriyaki sauce served with lemon and toasted halved Brussel sprouts drizzled with garlic olive oil.	Oven baked sweet potato patties served on ½ cup quinoa, drizzled with garlic olive oil. Sliced cucumber and tomato salad with vinegar and salt

Remember that your plan depends on your goals combined with the needs of your body. Talk to your doctor about what is right for you.

IMPORTANCE OF SIMPLICITY

When preparing and eating food becomes too complicated, food starts to take on a bigger place in life than it should. Cook something fancy when you want but keep it simple on a regular basis.

EAT TO LIVE. DON'T LIVE TO EAT

Food can be enjoyable, but it there to support and sustain your life, not to entertain you. Return food to the place it should plan in your life, keeping you alive!

> NOTE: if you like a food so much that you have trouble eating it with control, it has no place in your food plan until you have been doing this for long enough to change that reality.
>
> IF YOU CAN'T EAT A FOOD WITH CONTROL
>
> IT DOESN'T' BELONG IN YOUR DIET AT ALL
>
> Denial is always a part of the things we can't control very well.
>
> We don't like to admit we have a problem with bread or sugar or chips or pizza.
>
> Admitting you struggle with a particular food or likely a list of them isn't always easy and neither is mentally agreeing to give them up. However, admitting you don't eat certain foods well is a game changer of acceptance and maturity for your body plan that can absolutely change the game. .
>

FOOD IS FOR LIFE; LIFE IS NOT FOR FOOD!

Let your joy come from life. Let food be there to sustain your life. Stay active. Stay busy. Stay involved in life. Most of the time, stay out of the kitchen, or wrapped up in thoughts of food. Stay actively involved in life until your hunger tells you it's time to eat.

An exception for me is the time I spend cooking with family. When I get a chance to cook with the kids, we love to create healthy meals together.

NOW, MAKE A PLAN FOR YOUR FIRST DAY. Planning one good day well will give you a default plan you can follow for success even when you have nothing else in mind.

MY PLAN FOR DAY ONE

When I get hungry in the morning, I will eat:

_____

_____

_____

_____

One snack I can have on hand when I need something is:

If I get hungry around midday, I will eat:

A later snack (if I need it) will be:

_____

_____

_____

For dinner I will eat:

_____

_____

_____

To lower your hours of consumption, consider not eating anything past 7 pm which a very powerful strategy that can change your ability to lose weight dramatically. To take this one step further consider intermittent fasting, which is cutting your window of eating even more. Both give your body a break from processing food so that it can rest and recharge itself, and both give it time to burn the food you have in your system before you go to bed, so you can lose weight easier at night.

Eating may give us the energy and building blocks we need for life, but it is also a labor-intensive process from which our bodies need rest.

PREVENT INSULIN RESISTANCE BY GIVING YOUR BODY A BREAK

When you have food in your digestive system, your body must produce insulin so you can use it. If you always keep food in your stomach 24/7 your body is constantly flooded with insulin. When they are constantly exposed to it, our bodies sometimes build up a resistance to insulin. To help prevent this, consider giving your body 12 hours of digestive downtime a day so it can recharge and regulate its response to sugar.

Digesting food is important, but it is also hard to do.

Just like we do, our bodies need a break from their job of

Digestion so they rest, do other tasks get ready to do it again.

Research with both humans and animals shows that when we feed ourselves on more of an intermittent schedule, we stay sharper, age slower and add years of productive time to our lives. We don't work 24/7. We need some daily time off to rest and recharge from our work and so do our bodies. Don't keep them so full that it takes all night to digest that food as well.

Consider that it is healthy to give our bodies a break from food at times and realize you will live longer and feel better and give your bodies a break from insulin when you do.

Shaelee is one of my six amazing kids, all pictured here except my son who was taking the shot. Shaelee and I began in different places, and of course, we will end in different places physically as well, but we are both strong believers in the power of mindset to change our lives and where we are with our bodies.

I fought a battle with weight for decades. Shaelee developed a love of fitness that took her to a different level.

IN CONCLUSION,

You've got this! It doesn't matter where you start, only that you commit to sticking with it until the end.

If I did it, so can you.

MINDSET CHANGES THE GAME

Your body mindset is the lens through which you see the physical side of your life. It affects your emotions, your competence, your resilience, and your success. Like sunglass lenses, the mental filters you see things through change the way you experience them.

Don't waste another precious year in a body you're not happy with

I did it, and you can too!

You deserve to experience your own potential!

Me and my girls.

This picture was taken just after my body makeover and just before Shaelee started hers. It is missing only my son, Brandon.

YOU'VE GOT THIS!

You have what it takes to dramatically change your body. You have what it takes to do it and you always have.

Mindset changes you and it changes the success of your goals. It changes the relationship you have with food and fitness. It changes the way you experience the process, but most importantly it change the way you see and feel about you.

Mindset can make s the relationship you have food and fitness a good one, so you live and quit battling with it in your mind. Mindset doesn't just improve your body. It improves everything about the way you approach and experience your life.

To get on track, get happy and achieve your goals you have to get in the mindset it takes to do it.

Mindset is the game changer in EVERY area of your life!

Mindset is incredibly powerful because it changes the game for you physically, and in every other area of your life. Of course, mindset will change you and your body.

There is nothing in this world
That a change of mindset can't improve!

Each mental place we are in, and each set of belief we have will lead to a specific set of outcomes. Mindset has cause/effect relationship with where we are in our lives.

One mindset gets you **HERE**.
Another mindset gets you **THERE**.

I had to get my head in a different place to finally end the self-defeating things I was doing to my body. I had to change the mental image I had of myself and overcome the roadblocks in my head to get where I am now. Shaelee had to change her mental image, too. She took it to a whole different level. Even in a physical journey like the two of us have been on, we found that ultimately, it is your mind and your thoughts that will get you there.

Now, after years of being a mom and a teacher, I am settling into my role as a grandma and Shaelee into hers as a teacher, fitness coach, and mother. It has been an amazing experience to come together with her on this beautiful project.

I hope that between our two perspectives, you can find a voice that speaks to you and inspires you find the mindset you need to change your relationship with food and fitness.

My final advice to you is that if I can do this, so can you!

My closing words of advice to you are these: if you get your head in the right place and don't allow discouragement, there is nothing you can't do. You have the power to do amazing things. That power must come from inside you. Get your head in the right place and you will change your body and your experience with the world around you completely.

There are no glass ceilings that can limit who you are and what you can do. Refuse to let your mind put a limit on what you or your body can do. Never underestimate the power of getting your mind in a different place with something! It changes how you feel or the power you have within your control. You can be and do anything! You just need to get your head in the place it takes to get you there!

There is nothing in life that will give you more

power over your diet, your body or anything else.

Get intentional about Mindset you need for the results that you want in many areas of your life because with the right mindset,

THE POWER OF MINDSET IS UNIVERSAL
USE IT TO BUILD YOU UP AND MAKE
YOU STRONG. USE IT TO GET INTENTIONAL
ABOUT WHAT YOU WANT AND KEEP YOU
FROM FALLING IN OTHER
AREAS OF YOUR LIFE AS WELL.
Your mind can change your body, or anything else in your life.
Get in the right mental place in your life, and use the universal
POWER OF MINDSET TO GET WHERE YOU WANT TO GO!

Changing the way you see yourself and everything else doesn't just change you physically, it changes you, your life, and your life experiences entirely! Mindset is the game changer of our lives!

Finding the best way to see things is your superpower. Get your head in the place it needs to get yourself on track toward the places you mentally and physically really want to go.

Tina R Allen

The Body Mindset

SUMMARY:

The main reason we lose control is that we lose clarity and when we do, we start to eat from impulse, emotion, or convenience.

The fix for the crazy uncertainty of life is INSANE CLARITY. When you get insanely clear about what you want and how you are going to get there, you can stay on track amid almost anything.

Knowing exactly what you must do every day and committing to do that in your mind without fail or excuse will get you there absolutely every time. When you make a plan that is so clear that you know you simply need to eat these things and do this one workout that day and it will work, then you will.

1. Make the right kind of decision to do it.
2. Get into the place of power in your head.
3. Commit to the right mindset.
4. Make an insanely clear plan about what to do.
5. Mentally wrap your head around where you are going and GET OKAY with what you have agreed to do to get there. Initial clarity and acceptance of what you are going to do takes away the struggle and drama and battle you would likely have with yourself over trying to get out of it later.

Thank you so much for joining us in this amazing adventure of getting your head in the place it takes to get the body and life you want to have. We appreciate you, our reader, and hope that our journey and connection with you has only just begun.

WINNING BODY-MINDSET STRATEGIES

- Visualize yourself winning.
- Let healthy living be a quality-of-life choice you enjoy, instead of something you should but don't want to do.
- Visualize yourself as a person who is in the middle of an inspiring body transformation.
- Visualize the things happening inside your body. For example, imagine the fat dropping off your body while you are asleep on the days you go to bed a little bit hungry. Imagine the fat and toxins leaving your body in sweat when you work out.
- BUILD ON YOUR SUCCESS. Tell yourself you have come too far to quit now.
- Remind yourself that THE HARD PART at the beginning doesn't last very long.
- Picture starving a bad bug out of your digestive system by refusing to give it the carbs it craves. Picture yourself replacing the colony of bad bugs that cause your cravings with a healthy ecosystem of probiotics from eating live fruits and vegetables.
- Starve those bad bugs out for ten days and think of eating as an antibiotic for your gut.
- Relish the feeling of physical challenge, even the lightness and drive you get from hunger.
- Alternate average healthy days with super fat burning days to make fast progress.
- Picture your body rebuilding a muscle when you have pushed beyond what it normally does.
- Our body only rejuvenates and builds muscles we use.
- Get your heart rate up and see how long you can keep it there. Add a minute or few seconds per day. Make it a contest.
- While doing that, see how many days in a row you can eat clean, workout, and stay on track. Set personal best records and then see if you can break them.

- Once you have established what those rules and routines are and accept them, make a NO EXCUSE POLICY for them.
- To stay on track toward your goals, quit considering the possibility of not doing it 'just for today.' Don't allow excuses. When you have a no excuse policy, no excuse is good enough to keep you from the things you decided you were going to do.
- Keep your word, especially to yourself.
- Don't exhaust your willpower by considering every opportunity to leave the path. Keep your eyes on where you are going and what you get to eat and do, as opposed to the things you don't. In other words, look away and don't even consider then.
- Protect yourself from COMMITMENT FATIGUE by making a ONE-TIME DECISION and letting it stay made in your head.
- As you get better and more able, use that NEW EVIDENCE to CHANGE THE VIEWS YOU HAVE OF YOURSELF. Become a doer of these things in your mind.
- Begin to see healthy food and fitness as something you enjoy.
- Don't allow thoughts of discouragement. If you keep going, it will work. The process is not always linear, but if you stick with it, it will work. It is scientifically impossible for your body to not lose weight or get fit in long run if you refuse to quit.
- Aim for continuous improvement instead of perfection.
- See your mistakes as data that has information yo can learn from. Each slip in life contains a piece of information you need for the puzzle of success.

> You've got this! Life if about the choice to continually keep growing and getting better in mind and body. In the right mindset, you will choose to grow until you are mentally, physically, and emotionally becoming the way you want to be.

ASK YOURSELF,

ARE YOU IN THE MENTAL PLACE
IT TAKES TO GET THIS DONE?

JOIN US ONLINE OR AT A RETREAT IN UTAH

Just a reminder that we are there for you, and you don't have to do this thing alone! If you feel like you need help, reach out to us and we will help you find the right level of help for you.

If you would like us to, we would love to coach you ourselves or help you find one of our wonderful coaches who can.

We would also love to invite you to join us for a mindset retreat in Utah if you are looking for a get-away and a whole new start.

Please know how much we appreciate you, our reader. Thank you for joining us on this Body Mindset journey and being part of our mindset family. Join us online. Find coaching from us or others on **coachifyme.com.** Reach our blogs and find us on YouTube. Join Shaelee @Shaekaefitness and come see us in Utah if you can.

We hope to build an ongoing relationship with you, our readers, and we would love to meet you and connect with you more in the future.

In the meantime, keep eating right, working out, and getting your mind in the place that will keep you powerful, make you love the process and give you the determination it takes to reach your goals!

In other words, keep your mind in the place it takes to get and keep the body and life that you want! Thank you for joining us on the amazing journey of **USING THE POWER OF YOUR MIND TO IMPROVE YOUR BODY!**

Tina R Allen,

Shaelee K. Phillips,

The Body Mindset

Thank you so much for joining in this journey. Please consider helping us and other readers out by giving us a review on Amazon.

WORKOUT BECAUSE YOU LOVE YOUR BODY, AND
THE LIFE YOU HAVE WHEN YOU DO

EAT RIGHT BECAUSE YOU LOVE GOOD FOOD AND
THE WAY YOU FEEL WHEN YOU DO.

THINK RIGHT BECAUSE IT GIVES YOU
POWER AND MOTIVATION TO DO RIGHT
AND BECAUSE YOU LOVE THE WAY
YOU FEEL WHEN YOU DO.

SEE YOURSELF, YOUR ABILITY AND
YOUR FOOD AND FITNESS IN THE
RIGHT WAY AND YOU WILL GET
A BODY YOU LOVE TO BE IN.

Printed in Great Britain
by Amazon

59102149R00169